Contents

© HMH Supplemental Publishers Inc. All rights reserved.

Summarizing Strategies Grade 5, SV 9781419099892

Introduction

Throughout their school career, students are asked to read a variety of materials, from long stories and challenging poems to brief, informative articles and in-depth reports. Regardless of the genre and length of what they read, students must be able to summarize new information. A *summary* is a brief statement that tells the important points of a work of fiction or the main ideas of a work of nonfiction.

Summarizing is a fundamental reading and study skill. Young readers who master this skill have a powerful tool that helps them
- check their comprehension of what they have read.
- create their own materials for later study and review.
- organize information in various patterns.
- paraphrase new information in words that are meaningful to them.
- perform better on standardized test items that require summary.

Not only does summarizing help students gauge their reading comprehension, it reveals the underlying organizational patterns of writing. Students can then use these patterns as they write their own fiction and nonfiction pieces.

In early grades, summarizing is often taught in conjunction with identifying main idea and important details. As students progress, they learn to extract important information from a greater variety of genres and to generalize, draw conclusions, and make inferences as part of summarizing.

This series, *Summarizing Strategies,* is comprised of five books (Grades 2–6) and suggests a variety of techniques to encourage summarizing skill development. Each book targets 21 different strategies and employs a diverse collection of graphic organizers to assist students in visualizing how summaries are formed. Graphic organizers are critical components that serve as scaffolding necessary for students to structure their summaries and make connections between the targeted strategy and summarizing.

The strategies are logically sequenced from most basic to most difficult. Students begin by looking for the main idea and supporting details. As they progress through the book, students will encounter increasingly complex skills that require them to use higher-order thinking skills.

© HMH Supplemental Publishers Inc. All rights reserved.

Features

Each of the 21 strategies follows a four-page sequence. The first page contains a completed model graphic organizer and summary based on the targeted strategy.

Students first learn about the strategy they will practice.

Sample reading selection is geared toward targeted summarizing strategy.

A completed model is provided for students to follow.

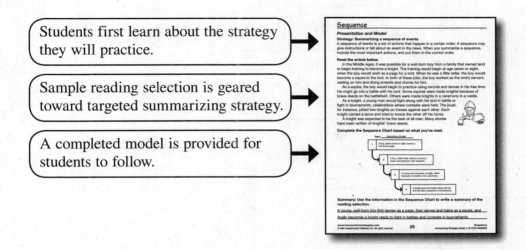

The second and third pages of each section provide reading passages adapted for each strategy. After reading each story, students continue to the worksheet page to complete the graphic organizer and write a summary based on what they have read in the story.

Students may practice reading independently, in small groups, or with the whole class.

Simple, clean designs and illustrations allow for clear photocopies and easy-to-read transparencies.

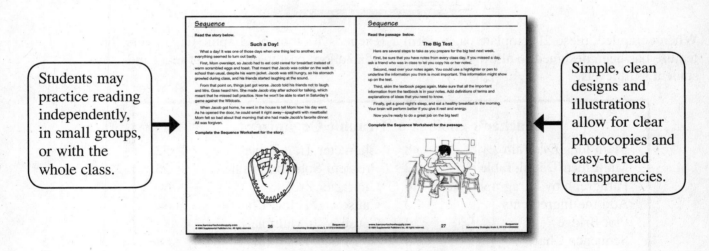

The fourth page in each section is a worksheet featuring a specific graphic organizer created for each strategy. These worksheets are designed for use with the provided texts as well as any other readings the teacher may choose, allowing for extra practice as needed. Worksheet pages are easily found by looking for the Teacher's Toolbox icon:

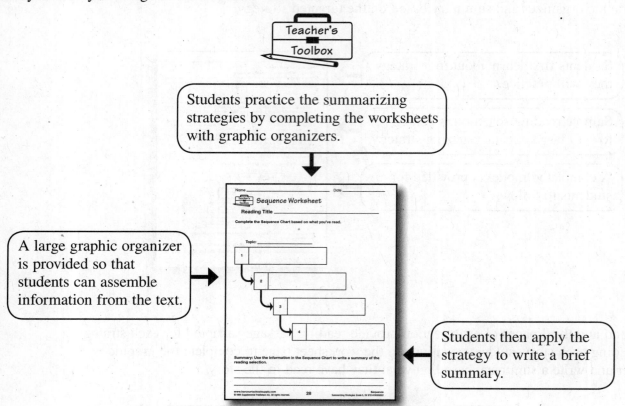

Teacher's Toolbox

Students practice the summarizing strategies by completing the worksheets with graphic organizers.

A large graphic organizer is provided so that students can assemble information from the text.

Students then apply the strategy to write a brief summary.

When compiled, these 21 template pages form a Teacher's Toolbox of Graphic Organizers. This feature has been designed to allow flexibility and adaptation for a wide range of texts and student skill levels.

Teacher's Toolbox of Graphic Organizers

Summarizing Strategies uses a variety of techniques to improve students' abilities to summarize. With continued practice in summarizing, students should improve their reading comprehension skills and standardized test scores.

Main Idea

Presentation and Model

Strategy: Finding and stating the main idea of what you read

When you state the main idea of something you have read, you are writing a one-sentence summary. The main idea is the most important idea in a reading selection. To find this important idea, follow these steps:

Read: Read the paragraphs carefully.

Ask: What topic are the paragraphs about?

Decide: What do all the sentences say about the topic?

Read the article below.

An alligator waits on the bank of a stream or in shallow water, appearing to be asleep. Ducks, rabbits, and other small animals may come near it. Suddenly, the alligator lashes out with its tail to kill the creature. It gobbles down its prey in one quick bite. There is no doubt about it—the alligator is sly when it comes to catching food.

Alligators may look sleepy and slow, but they can move quickly when they must. Even though adult alligators can weigh more than 800 pounds, they can run very fast for short periods of time. In fact, they can reach speeds of up to 35 miles per hour!

Alligators are shy around people, but they will defend their territory. If you see an alligator, don't approach it. Remember—it may not really be sleeping!

Complete the Main Idea Diagram based on what you've read.

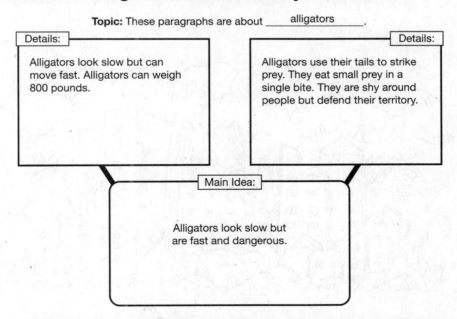

Topic: These paragraphs are about _____alligators_____.

Details:
Alligators look slow but can move fast. Alligators can weigh 800 pounds.

Details:
Alligators use their tails to strike prey. They eat small prey in a single bite. They are shy around people but defend their territory.

Main Idea:
Alligators look slow but are fast and dangerous.

Summary: Use the information in the Main Idea Diagram to write a summary of the reading selection.

Alligators may look slow and sleepy, but they are fast, dangerous hunters.

www.harcourtschoolsupply.com
© HMH Supplemental Publishers Inc. All rights reserved.
5
Main Idea
Summarizing Strategies Grade 5, SV 9781419099892

Main Idea

Read the article below.

Earthquakes

Many earthquakes occur every year, but you don't read about most of them in the newspaper. This is because most earthquakes do very little damage. Some of them, however, can destroy cities and hurt many people. Earthquakes on the floor of the ocean can cause huge waves, called tsunamis, to speed toward land where they can cause tremendous damage.

The worst earthquake in the history of the United States happened in San Francisco in 1906. Although the earthquake did knock down buildings, most of the damage to the city was done by fires that broke out as a result of the earthquake. Firefighters could not reach the burning buildings, and water lines were broken so that fire hoses had nothing to spray. Many people perished, and $500,000,000 worth of property was destroyed.

Complete the Main Idea Worksheet for the article.

© HMH Supplemental Publishers Inc. All rights reserved.

Main Idea

Read the article below.

Food Fuel

Food is fuel for our bodies. The fuel value of food is measured in calories. An apple has 75 calories, and a cup of peanuts has 805 calories. That means that the peanuts furnish a lot more heat and energy for the body than the apple does.

Most children need about 2,000 calories a day. If more calories are eaten than the body needs, the body stores the fuel as fat. If not enough food is eaten, the body uses up fat, or other body cells, since it must have fuel.

Foods with the most calories are not necessarily the best for your body. For example, both a cola drink and a banana have about 100 calories. However, the banana has other nutrients that help the body stay healthy. The cola does not.

Complete the Main Idea Worksheet for the article.

© HMH Supplemental Publishers Inc. All rights reserved.
Summarizing Strategies Grade 5, SV 9781419099892

Name _____   Date _____

Teacher's Toolbox

Main Idea Worksheet

Reading Title _____

Complete the Main Idea Diagram based on what you've read.

Topic: These paragraphs are about _____.

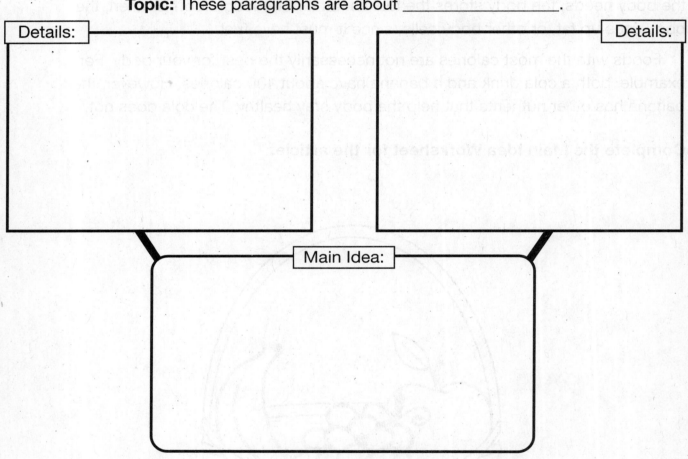

Details:

Details:

Main Idea:

Summary: Use the information in the Main Idea Diagram to write a summary of the reading selection.

_____
_____
_____

© HMH Supplemental Publishers Inc. All rights reserved.
Main Idea
Summarizing Strategies Grade 5, SV 9781419099892

Supporting Details

Presentation and Model

Strategy: Finding and understanding the purpose of details in what you read

The main idea is the most important idea in a reading. Details give specific information about the main idea by answering questions such as: *who, when, where,* or *how*. Good summaries include main ideas and the most important details from the reading.

Read the article below.

When boats and ships come into a harbor, how are they instructed where to go? Cars on streets and highways follow painted lines and dashes to stay in the right place, but you cannot paint the water. What prevents boats and ships in a busy harbor from colliding with each other or running into rocks under the water?

Buoys guide boats and ships safely in and out of harbors. Buoys are floating objects that help sailors and boaters steer safely through tricky waters near shore. Some buoys show that the water is too shallow for boats. Others warn of rocks or mark the paths that boats must follow to safely enter the harbor. Buoys may have bells, whistles, or flashing lights that get sailors' attention. No harbor, large or small, is complete without buoys.

Complete the Main Idea/Detail Table based on what you've read.

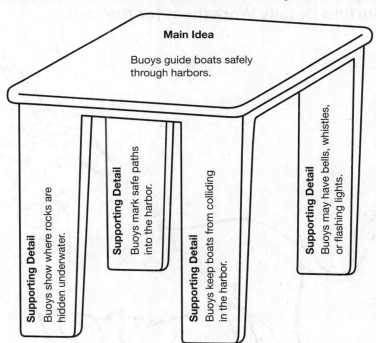

Main Idea

Buoys guide boats safely through harbors.

Supporting Detail Buoys show where rocks are hidden underwater.

Supporting Detail Buoys mark safe paths into the harbor.

Supporting Detail Buoys keep boats from colliding in the harbor.

Supporting Detail Buoys may have bells, whistles, or flashing lights.

Summary: Use the information in the Main Idea/Detail Table to write a summary of the reading selection.

Buoys help boats sail safely in harbors. They warn of underwater dangers. They

prevent collisions.

© HMH Supplemental Publishers Inc. All rights reserved.

Supporting Details

Read the article below.

All About Myths

Myths and true stories have different kinds of characters, events, and messages. First, the characters in myths are not real. They might be monsters, sprites, or people with impossible powers, such as the power to fly. In true stories, the characters are people much like you.

Second, myths include events that could never really happen. A person with supernatural powers may lift a mountain, for example, or ride a unicorn. In true stories, all the events are things that could really happen, and there are no imaginary creatures.

Finally, myths often teach a lesson. For example, when a brave hero wins a battle, the lesson might be that good will defeat evil. True stories, on the other hand, may or may not teach a lesson. Both kinds of stories, however, can be fun to read.

Complete the Supporting Details Worksheet for the article.

© HMH Supplemental Publishers Inc. All rights reserved.
Summarizing Strategies Grade 5, SV 9781419099892

Supporting Details

Read the article below.

Almost Human

People have always enjoyed comparing animal activity to human behavior. As a result, animals have come to stand for certain things. The bee, for example, works continuously, producing honey and helping flowers grow. Therefore, some people feel that the bee stands for hard work.

Swans move smoothly across ponds and lakes. For this reason, swans have become symbols for beauty and grace. Another animal, the snail, has come to symbolize slowness, because it moves so slowly.

The butterfly symbolizes the process of life itself. This is because butterflies go through four complete changes in their life cycle—from egg, to caterpillar, to chrysalis, to full-grown butterfly.

Complete the Supporting Details Worksheet for the article.

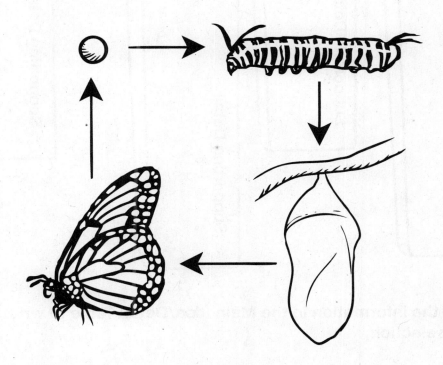

© HMH Supplemental Publishers Inc. All rights reserved.

Teacher's Toolbox

Name _____ Date _____

Supporting Details Worksheet

Reading Title _____

Complete the Main Idea/Detail Table based on what you've read.

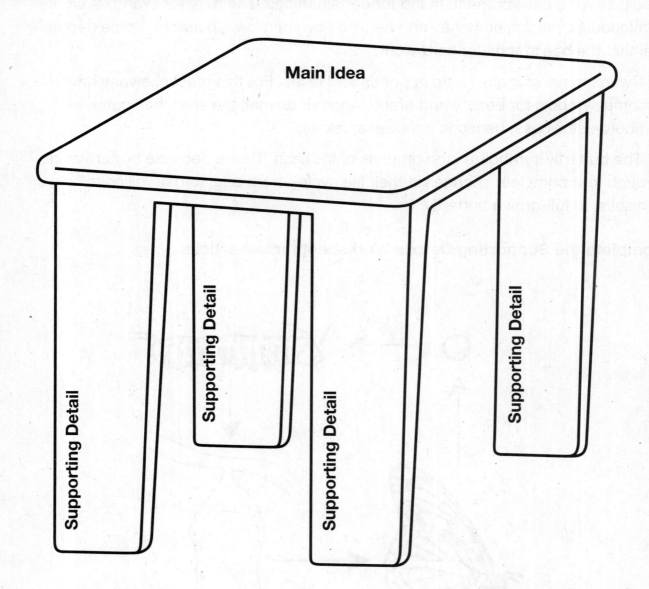

Main Idea

Supporting Detail

Supporting Detail

Supporting Detail

Supporting Detail

Summary: Use the information in the Main Idea/Detail Table to write a summary of the reading selection.

_____

_____

_____

© HMH Supplemental Publishers Inc. All rights reserved.
12
Supporting Details
Summarizing Strategies Grade 5, SV 9781419099892

Creating a Summary

Presentation and Model

Strategy: Understanding what it means to summarize and how summarizing helps you learn

When you write a summary, you write a short statement that tells the main facts of what you have read. A summary can also tell the main events of a story you have read. Summaries do not include most of the details in what you read—just the most important facts. Summarizing is a useful skill, which may help you understand, remember, and study what you have read.

Read the story below.

Tony was having a wonderful birthday! He had a party at school, and his mom brought cupcakes for the whole class. On the bus ride home, Tony's best friend, Markus, gave him a remote-control airplane, something he had always wanted. They agreed to try it out that afternoon in the park.

When Tony came home from park, what a surprise awaited him! His mother had invited all of his cousins, aunts, and uncles over for a party and cookout. They played music and danced in the backyard, and Tony opened a few more presents.

By the end of the day, Tony was tired but happy, especially because he knew his birthday celebration was not over yet. His dad had promised to take him to the amusement park that weekend to ride the big roller coaster!

Complete the Paragraph by Paragraph Chart based on what you've read.

Paragraph	Summary
1	Tony celebrated his birthday at school and received a present from his best friend.
2	Tony's mother threw a surprise party for him.
3	Tony looked forward to going to the amusement park on the weekend.

Summary: Use the information in the Paragraph by Paragraph Chart to write a summary of the reading selection.

Tony had a fun birthday with a celebration at school and a party at home. Then he looked forward to going to the amusement park with his dad.

© HMH Supplemental Publishers Inc. All rights reserved.
Summarizing Strategies Grade 5, SV 9781419099892

Creating a Summary

Read the story below.

The Campfire

Mr. Saucedo and his daughter, Julia, were camping in the park. They had just finished setting up the tent. It was time to cook dinner! Julia had never cooked over an open fire.

Mr. Saucedo showed Julia how to make a fire. First, they found a flat spot on the ground and cleared away the loose leaves and sticks. They made a circle of rocks to keep the fire in a small space. They also collected small sticks, dry moss, and some larger pieces of wood they found lying around.

Julia put the moss and small sticks in the circle of rocks. Then Mr. Saucedo used his magnifying glass to focus the sunlight on the moss. The hot beam set the moss on fire. When the pile of sticks was burning well, he added some larger sticks and small logs. Once the fire was going, Mr. Saucedo gave Julia a long, slender stick. They had fun roasting hot dogs over the campfire.

Complete the Creating a Summary Worksheet for the story.

© HMH Supplemental Publishers Inc. All rights reserved.
Summarizing Strategies Grade 5, SV 9781419099892

Creating a Summary

Read the article below.

Plant Your Garden

When preparing to plant a garden, first choose a spot of ground where plants will grow well. The ground should be fairly fertile. It should get plenty of sunshine as well. Pick a spot where you can bring water to the plants.

After you have chosen a garden spot, get the soil ready for planting. Scatter fertilizer over the ground. Next, dig up the ground and break up any large clumps of dirt. Then, rake the soil until it is fine and the garden plot is level.

Now you are ready to plant some seeds. Dig small holes in straight rows. Place seeds an equal distance apart, as instructed on the seed packet. Cover the seeds with soil. If it does not rain, water the garden gently. Soon you should see your plants beginning to sprout.

Complete the Creating a Summary Worksheet for the article.

© HMH Supplemental Publishers Inc. All rights reserved.

Name _____ Date _____

Creating a Summary Worksheet

Reading Title _____

Complete the Paragraph by Paragraph Chart based on what you've read.

Paragraph	Summary
1	
2	
3	

Summary: Use the information in the Paragraph by Paragraph Chart to write a summary of the reading selection.

_____

_____

_____

© HMH Supplemental Publishers Inc. All rights reserved.
Summarizing Strategies Grade 5, SV 9781419099892

Theme

Presentation and Model

Strategy: Understanding and identifying theme in a story you read

In works of fiction the overall idea is called the **theme.** The theme is the idea about life or the way people behave that the author wants you to think about.

Read the story below.

Greg was furious. A group of boys had invited Greg to go to the movies with them, but Greg's mother had said he couldn't go. She didn't like the idea of boys his age going to the movies without an adult. Angrily, Greg stormed up to his room and shut himself in.

"It's not fair," he steamed. "When I get to school tomorrow, my friends will make fun of me because I couldn't go." He imagined how embarrassed he'd feel the next day.

Still, maybe his mother was right. The movie didn't end until after dark, and the walk home was several blocks. He shivered as he thought of making that walk by himself. But what was more important—being a little scared, or being embarrassed at school?

The next morning, Greg hurried to eat breakfast and get out of the house without talking to his mother. When he got to school, there were his friends. They looked unhappy.

"What's up, guys?" Greg asked. "Was the movie terrible?"

"Our parents didn't let us go!" one said. "They said we need an adult with us. So I guess we'll have to ask one of our parents to go along."

Quickly, Greg said, "I bet my mom will go!" And somehow he knew she would.

Complete the Add the Ingredients diagram based on what you've read.

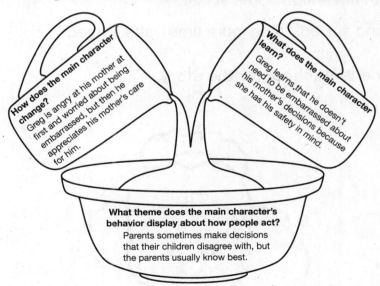

How does the main character change?
Greg is angry at his mother at first and worried about being embarrassed, but then he appreciates his mother's care for him.

What does the main character learn?
Greg learns that he doesn't need to be embarrassed about his mother's decisions because she has his safety in mind.

What theme does the main character's behavior display about how people act?
Parents sometimes make decisions that their children disagree with, but the parents usually know best.

Summary: Use the information in the Add the Ingredients diagram to write a summary of the reading selection.

Sometimes children resent their parents' decisions, as Greg did, but children

eventually realize that their parents just want what is best for their children.

© HMH Supplemental Publishers Inc. All rights reserved.
Summarizing Strategies Grade 5, SV 9781419099892

Theme

Read the story below.

Oh, No! Not Again!

Sondra had lived in many places. Her dad had to move to where his job sent him, so Sondra's family never stayed in one place very long. She was born in California, and they had stayed there until she was three years old. Then came a move to Oregon, followed by a move to Washington, where Sondra started school. She made friends, of course, but they didn't last because soon the family was off to a new location. In five school years, Sondra had moved three times. She always missed their old home in California.

So when her father told her that they were moving yet again, Sondra was very sad. "Dad, I've just gotten used to my new school," she complained. "I have friends. Please. I don't want to move again."

Her father sat by her on the couch and put his arm around her shoulders. He sighed. "I know how hard this has been on you," he admitted. "We moved a lot when I was a kid, too. But I have good news. This will be the last move. My company has promoted me to a permanent job at the home office back in California! We'll all get to go back and live by our old friends again. So let's do this one more time, and then we'll be home at last."

Sondra nodded and smiled. "One more time," she agreed.

Complete the Theme Worksheet for the story.

© HMH Supplemental Publishers Inc. All rights reserved.
Summarizing Strategies Grade 5, SV 9781419099892

Theme

Read the story below.

What a Mess!

"Aunt Linda!" called Sara. "I can't find my gym bag. Do you know where it is?"

"I haven't seen it, honey," her aunt said, stepping into Sara's bedroom. "But I think I know why you lost it. Look at this place!"

Sara looked around her room. What a mess! Clothes, books, and CD cases were scattered all over the floor. Drawers were open and overflowing with socks and shirts. The closet door couldn't close, because it was blocked by a pile of mismatched shoes. "Now I'll miss the bus for sure," she muttered.

Aunt Linda glanced behind the bed. "Is that it?"

"Yes, great—thanks!" Sara said as she ran for the door.

"Clean up when you get home!" called her aunt after her.

After school, Sara slouched home. She dreaded having to clean up the terrible mess she'd made in her room. Sara worked all afternoon on her room. "Why didn't I just clean up a little every day?" she thought. "I'll never let the mess get this bad again."

After her bath that night, Sara put her dirty clothes in the hamper and her shoes in the closet. As she got in bed, she knew that the next day she could do whatever she wanted after school because she had taken care of her room. She knew that putting a little effort into cleaning every day was the way to do it.

Complete the Theme Worksheet for the story.

© HMH Supplemental Publishers Inc. All rights reserved.
Summarizing Strategies Grade 5, SV 9781419099892

Name _____ Date _____

Teacher's
Toolbox

Theme Worksheet

Reading Title _____

Complete the Add the Ingredients diagram based on what you've read.

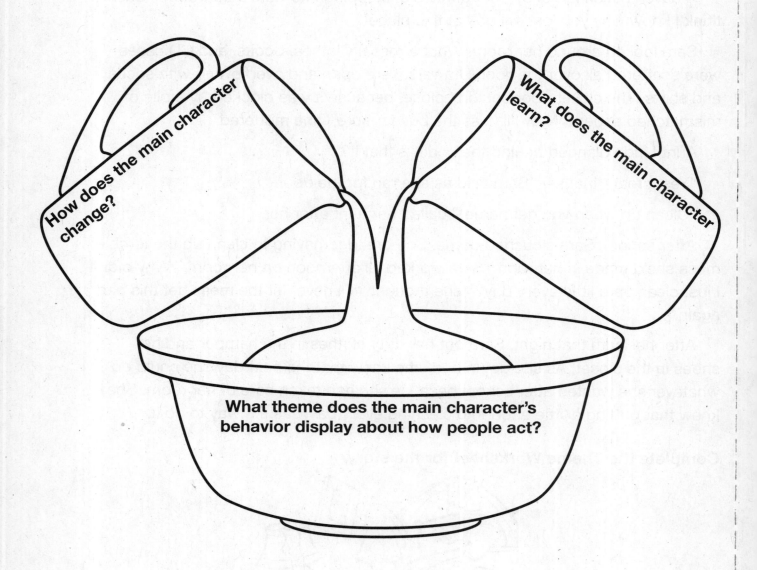

How does the main character change?

What does the main character learn?

What theme does the main character's behavior display about how people act?

Summary: Use the information in the Add the Ingredients diagram to write a summary of the reading selection.

_____

_____

_____

Plot

Presentation and Model

Strategy: Finding the main events of a story to summarize the plot

When you list the main events of a story, you make a plot summary. To find the main events of a story, ask these questions:

- What do the story's characters want or need?
- What is keeping the characters from getting what they want or need?
- How do the characters get what they want or need?

Read the story below.

Jody and Josh stood outside the old house. The paint was peeling from the outside of the house. Jody and Josh felt a little scared because the house looked so spooky.

Jody and Josh's mom had given them a loaf of bread to take to a friend who lived in the house. But they did not want to go knock on the door of the rickety old place.

"Let's go," said Josh bravely. Together, they walked up the shabby steps and knocked on the door. The door squeaked as someone opened it. A woman with a bright, friendly smile stood in the doorway. The smell of fresh paint floated out.

"Come on in!" said the woman. "You must be Jody and Josh. I'm sorry about the mess, but we just bought this old house, and are trying to fix it up!"

The house was not haunted! Jody and Josh felt relieved, and glad to have helped.

Complete the Plot Bridge based on what you've read.

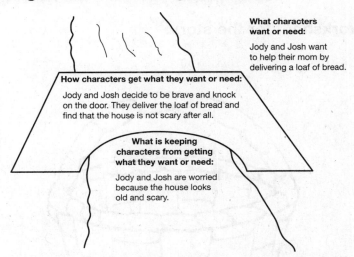

What characters want or need:

Jody and Josh want to help their mom by delivering a loaf of bread.

How characters get what they want or need:

Jody and Josh decide to be brave and knock on the door. They deliver the loaf of bread and find that the house is not scary after all.

What is keeping characters from getting what they want or need:

Jody and Josh are worried because the house looks old and scary.

Summary: Use the information in the Plot Bridge to write a summary of the reading selection.

Jody and Josh are scared to deliver a loaf of bread to a scary old house. They decide to be brave and knock on the door. They discover that the house is not scary, and they give their neighbor the bread.

© HMH Supplemental Publishers Inc. All rights reserved.
Summarizing Strategies Grade 5, SV 9781419099892

Plot

Read the story below.

Mom's Birthday

Maria and Anna wanted to give their mother a special birthday present. At first, they were worried because they had saved only a little money. Then Maria remembered something. "Anna, our teacher taught us to make baskets out of reeds," she said. "We can make one for a present."

"That's a good idea," said Anna. The two girls used reeds to make a plain basket. But the basket seemed too plain for a birthday present. So the sisters took the basket to the flower shop. They looked at the pretty baskets on the shelves so that they could decide how to decorate their basket.

The florist saw the girls and walked over. "That's a fine basket," he said. "Where did you get it?"

The sisters explained that they had made it. The florist liked the basket so much that he made a deal with the sisters. "I will decorate this basket for you to give your mother if you will make one of your hand-made baskets for me." Anna and Maria hurried home, excited to make a second basket to trade for their mom's present.

Complete the Plot Worksheet for the story.

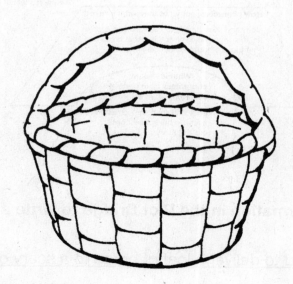

Plot

Read the story below.

Stage Fright

Kara put on the lacy dress that her mother had laid out on the bed. She brushed her hair carefully and tied it back with a ribbon. She looked in the mirror and sighed. "I look nice," she thought. "But will I play well?" She did not feel very sure of herself.

"Kara, come down," her father called. "It's time to leave for your piano recital."

As the family drove to the recital, Kara felt more and more nervous. "What if I play a wrong note?" she asked.

"Don't worry," said her mom. "Just keep playing and no one will remember the wrong note."

Still, Kara could not feel happy. At the recital, she sat with her friend Jaime. "Are you nervous?" she asked.

"A little," Jaime said. "Remember what our teacher says. When you feel nervous, it means that you have energy to play well!"

When Kara's turn came, she walked to big piano, sat down, and paused. She imagined that her nervous feelings were surges of energy. She played the first chord. Suddenly, she felt calm and happy. Before Kara knew it, she had finished playing. Now, instead of hearing her own nervous heartbeat, she heard the listeners clapping for her music.

Complete the Plot Worksheet for the story.

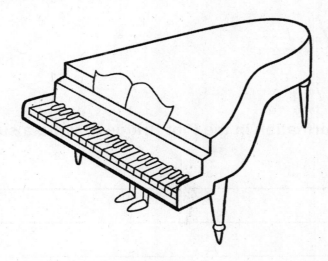

© HMH Supplemental Publishers Inc. All rights reserved.
Summarizing Strategies Grade 5, SV 9781419099892

Name _____   Date _____

Plot Worksheet

Reading Title _____

Complete the Plot Bridge based on what you've read.

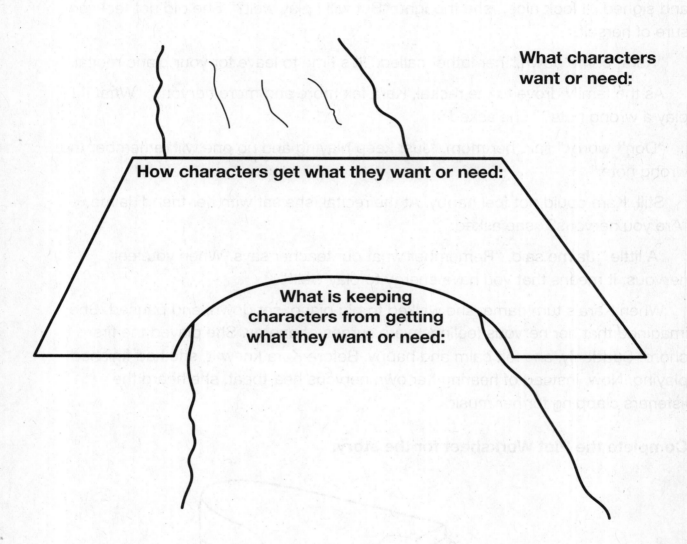

What characters want or need:

How characters get what they want or need:

What is keeping characters from getting what they want or need:

Summary: Use the information in the Plot Bridge to write a summary of the reading selection.

_____

_____

_____

© HMH Supplemental Publishers Inc. All rights reserved.
Summarizing Strategies Grade 5, SV 9781419099892

Sequence

Presentation and Model

Strategy: Summarizing a sequence of events

A sequence of events is a set of actions that happen in a certain order. A sequence may give instructions or tell about an event in the news. When you summarize a sequence, include the most important actions, and put them in the correct order.

Read the article below.

In the Middle Ages, it was possible for a well-born boy from a family that owned land to begin training to become a knight. The training would begin at age seven or eight, when the boy would work as a page for a lord. When he was a little older, the boy would become a squire to the lord. In both of these jobs, the boy worked as the lord's servant, waiting on him and doing errands and chores for him.

As a squire, the boy would begin to practice using swords and lances in his free time. He might go into a battle with his lord. Some squires were made knights because of brave deeds on the battlefield. Others were made knights in a ceremony in a castle.

As a knight, a young man would fight along with his lord in battle or fight in tournaments, celebrations where contests were held. The joust, for instance, pitted two knights on horses against each other. Each knight carried a lance and tried to knock the other off his horse.

A knight was expected to be the best of all men. Many stories have been written of knights' brave deeds.

Complete the Sequence Chart based on what you've read.

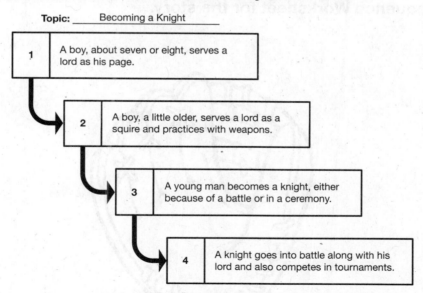

Topic: Becoming a Knight

1. A boy, about seven or eight, serves a lord as his page.

2. A boy, a little older, serves a lord as a squire and practices with weapons.

3. A young man becomes a knight, either because of a battle or in a ceremony.

4. A knight goes into battle along with his lord and also competes in tournaments.

Summary: Use the information in the Sequence Chart to write a summary of the reading selection.

A young, well-born boy first serves as a page, then serves and trains as a squire, and finally becomes a knight ready to fight in battles and compete in tournaments.

© HMH Supplemental Publishers Inc. All rights reserved.
Summarizing Strategies Grade 5, SV 9781419099892

Sequence

Read the story below.

Such a Day!

What a day! It was one of those days when one thing led to another, and everything seemed to turn out badly.

First, Mom overslept, so Jacob had to eat cold cereal for breakfast instead of warm scrambled eggs and toast. That meant that Jacob was colder on the walk to school than usual, despite his warm jacket. Jacob was still hungry, so his stomach growled during class, and his friends started laughing at the sound.

From that point on, things just got worse. Jacob told his friends not to laugh, and Mrs. Goss heard him. She made Jacob stay after school for talking, which meant that he missed ball practice. Now he won't be able to start in Saturday's game against the Wildcats.

When Jacob got home, he went in the house to tell Mom how his day went. As he opened the door, he could smell it right away—spaghetti with meatballs! Mom felt so bad about that morning that she had made Jacob's favorite dinner. All was forgiven.

Complete the Sequence Worksheet for the story.

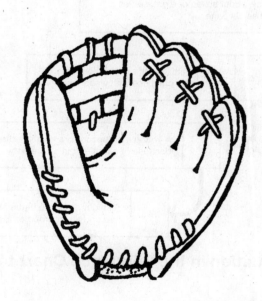

© HMH Supplemental Publishers Inc. All rights reserved.

Summarizing Strategies Grade 5, SV 9781419099892

Sequence

Read the passage below.

The Big Test

Here are several steps to take as you prepare for the big test next week.

First, be sure that you have notes from every class day. If you missed a day, ask a friend who was in class to let you copy his or her notes.

Second, read over your notes again. You could use a highlighter or pen to underline the information you think is most important. This information might show up on the test.

Third, skim the textbook pages again. Make sure that all the important information from the textbook is in your notes. Add definitions of terms and explanations of ideas that you need to know.

Finally, get a good night's sleep, and eat a healthy breakfast in the morning. Your brain will perform better if you give it rest and energy.

Now you're ready to do a great job on the big test!

Complete the Sequence Worksheet for the passage.

© HMH Supplemental Publishers Inc. All rights reserved.
Summarizing Strategies Grade 5, SV 9781419099892

Name _____ Date _____

Sequence Worksheet

Reading Title _____

Complete the Sequence Chart based on what you've read.

Topic: _____

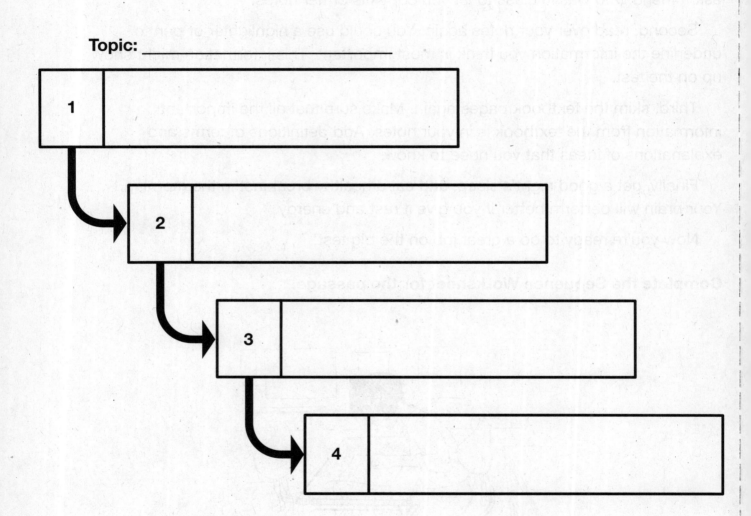

1

2

3

4

Summary: Use the information in the Sequence Chart to write a summary of the reading selection.

_____

_____

_____

www.harcourtschoolsupply.com
© HMH Supplemental Publishers Inc. All rights reserved.   **28**   Sequence
Summarizing Strategies Grade 5, SV 9781419099892

Creating a Story Web

Read the story below.

Autumn Leaves

Michael walked to the tool shed with a grumpy expression on his face. He had had plans for the afternoon—mostly, to play video games with his neighbor and good friend, Jin. But his dad had other plans.

Michael yanked the shed door open and grabbed the rake. "Why me?" he grumbled. "And why today? There are always leaves to rake." But since he had no choice, he decided to get the job done as quickly as possible.

Soon, the sound of the rake scraping the lawn and the steady, rhythmic movement of his arms calmed Michael down. He began to notice things—sounds, for instance. He heard cars on the street, children laughing in the yard next door, and birds singing. He became aware of the sound of the wind through the last leaves on the trees.

Then he noticed the pleasant, earthy smell of the crumbling brown and gold leaves. He studied the growing mound of leaves and remembered, suddenly, jumping in piles of leaves when he was young. "This isn't so bad after all," he thought. "I might even take one more jump into the leaves, just for fun."

Complete the Creating a Story Web Worksheet for the story.

Teacher's
Toolbox

Name _____ Date _____

Creating a Story Web Worksheet

Reading Title _____

Complete the Story Web based on what you've read.

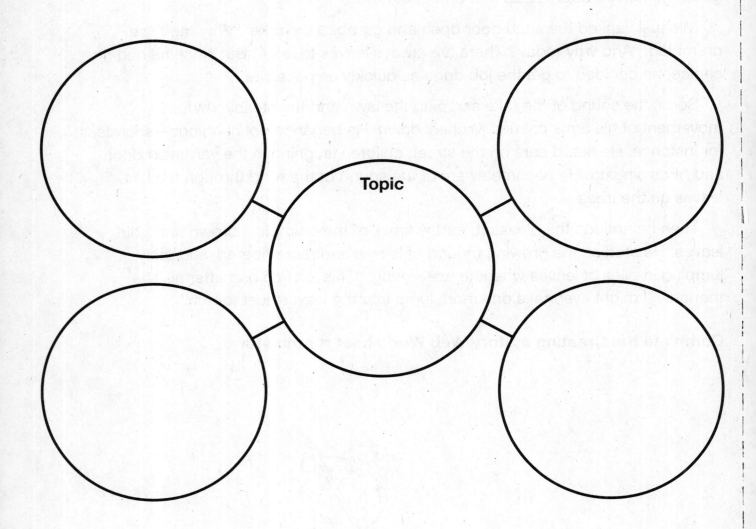

Topic

Summary: Use the information in the Story Web to write a summary of the reading selection.

_____

_____

© HMH Supplemental Publishers Inc. All rights reserved.

Implied Main Idea

Presentation and Model

Strategy: Finding implied main ideas in what you read

Often, writers state the main idea clearly. Other times, writers use an implied main idea. Implied means "suggested" or "hinted at."

Read the article below.

Kangaroos and their smaller cousins, wallabies, are native to Australia. A kangaroo carries its baby, called a joey, in a pouch on the front of its body. Kangaroos have a strong kick. They are grazers and live in groups.

Emus also live in Australia. These enormous birds are just a bit smaller than the ostrich. They weigh too much to fly, but they can run. Emus eat grass, flowers, insects, and just about anything else they can find.

Another animal found in Australia is the koala. Koalas live in trees and eat leaves that would make most animals ill. Koalas can eat these leaves because they digest them very slowly. In fact, koalas spend most of the day and night asleep.

But the oddest Australian animal of all is perhaps the platypus. It looks like a combination of a beaver, a duck, and an otter. It has fur like a mammal, but lays eggs like a bird or reptile.

Complete the Implied Main Idea Chart based on what you've read.

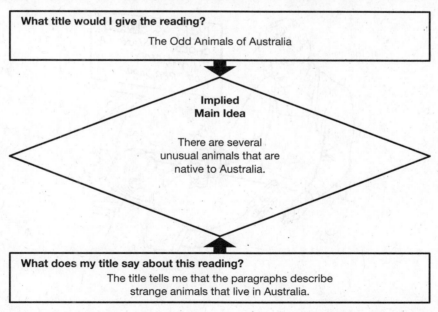

What title would I give the reading?
The Odd Animals of Australia

Implied Main Idea
There are several unusual animals that are native to Australia.

What does my title say about this reading?
The title tells me that the paragraphs describe strange animals that live in Australia.

Summary: Use the information in the Implied Main Idea Chart to write a summary of the reading selection. Include the implied main idea.

Some very unusual animals live in Australia. Kangaroos, emus, koalas, and

platypuses are unlike other animals and have odd behaviors and appearances.

Implied Main Idea

Read the passage below.

Dear Mr. Aggens

In my neighborhood, there is a small grocery store. It's just a block from my house, so I can walk there easily. A retired couple, Mr. and Mrs. Aggens, are the owners. They are both nice, but I always hope that Mr. Aggens will wait on me when I shop there.

Mr. Aggens is very friendly and full of smiles. When I buy ice cream, he always makes the scoops very large. He never hurries me when I'm trying to decide whether to spend my money on apples or fruit bars. And he sometimes offers me a new fruit to try.

What I like best about Mr. Aggens is that he doesn't rush his customers out of the store. After I make my purchases, I like to stay for a few minutes, enjoying the smell of freshly ground coffee and talking to Mr. Aggens. He's never too busy for conversation.

Complete the Implied Main Idea Worksheet for the passage.

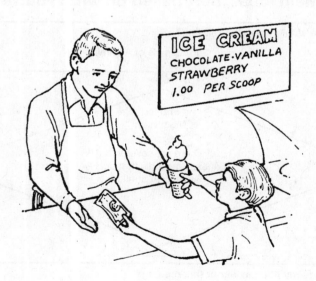

© HMH Supplemental Publishers Inc. All rights reserved.
Summarizing Strategies Grade 5, SV 9781419099892

Implied Main Idea

Read the story below.

The Campaign

Kay had sat, with decreasing patience, by the phone all afternoon. The students at her school had voted for the officers of the student council that day. Kay had run for the office of president of the group. In the past few days, she had passed out dozens of flyers telling everyone why she should be elected.

Kay had been the vice-president last year. She had learned a lot from that experience and had worked hard to make the school a better place for students and teachers. She knew she could do a good job as school president this year. Surely the other students could see what a good choice she was, but the other person running for office was also a good candidate.

Kay's big sister saw her by the phone. "Don't worry, Kay," she said. "No matter who wins, you did a great job running your campaign, and you should be proud."

Just as Kay began to reply, the phone rang. Kay answered it, struggling to keep her voice calm. She listened for a minute, then thanked the caller. As soon as she hung up, she gave a shout of joy. She had won the election!

Complete the Implied Main Idea Worksheet for the story.

© HMH Supplemental Publishers Inc. All rights reserved.

Summarizing Strategies Grade 5, SV 9781419099892

Name _____ Date _____

Teacher's
Toolbox

Implied Main Idea Worksheet

Reading Title _____

Complete the Implied Main Idea Chart based on what you've read.

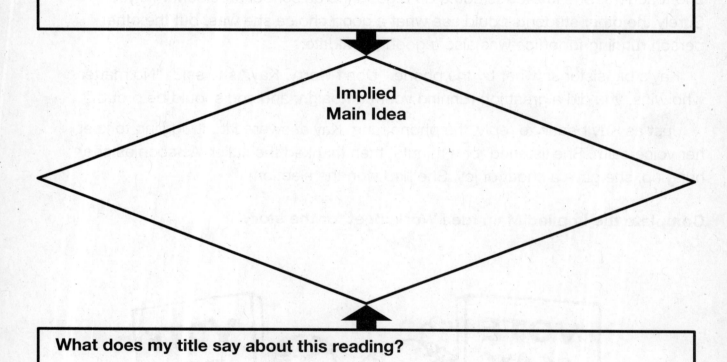

What title would I give the reading?

Implied
Main Idea

What does my title say about this reading?

Summary: Use the information in the Implied Main Idea Chart to write a summary of the reading selection. Include the implied main idea.

_____

_____

_____

Making and Supporting Predictions

Presentation and Model

Strategy: Predicting what will happen next in what you are reading

When you read a story, you keep track of the events that have already happened. You can also think ahead—you can make predictions about what will happen next. Making predictions keeps you engaged with the story and helps you understand the plot.

Read the story below.

Elena stood up, laundry basket at her feet, freshly washed towels in her arms. She had just seen a distant flash of lightning followed by the low rumble of thunder. A quick glance at the sky past the clothesline showed dark clouds rolling in from the east. Just an hour ago, the sun had been a huge orange ball in a blue sky, and the air had been hot enough to dry clothes. Now the early afternoon was beginning to turn gray and there was a smell of dampness in the air.

Elena sighed. Would the storm pass to the east, or would it come this way? She looked at all the damp clothes still in the basket. She could dry the clothes in the house, but nothing could beat the freshness of the outdoors.

Complete the Prediction Chart based on what you've read.

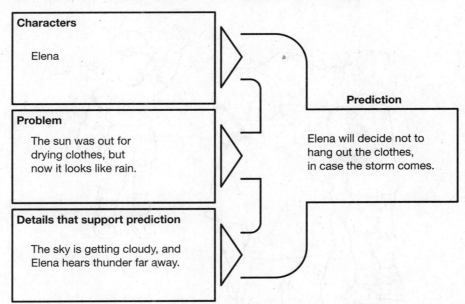

Characters

Elena

Problem

The sun was out for drying clothes, but now it looks like rain.

Details that support prediction

The sky is getting cloudy, and Elena hears thunder far away.

Prediction

Elena will decide not to hang out the clothes, in case the storm comes.

Summary: Use the information in the Prediction Chart to write a summary of the reading selection.

Elena is hanging the laundry out to dry, but a storm seems to be approaching. Elena must decide whether to hang the clothes outside or not.

Making and Supporting Predictions

Read the story below.

The Catcher's Mitt

Jill was very angry with her brother Clay. Both of them played ball on competitive teams, and Clay was always borrowing Jill's equipment. He did return it, but sometimes Jill needed whatever Clay had borrowed.

This time, Clay had borrowed Jill's favorite mitt. He had misplaced his own, and he wanted to practice catching with his friends at the park. The mitt was special to Jill because their big brother had sent it to her from overseas for her birthday.

When Clay got home, he realized that he'd forgotten the mitt in the park. He ran back to the field where he and his friends had practiced, but the mitt was gone. Clay felt terrible. Not only had he borrowed Jill's mitt without asking, now it was gone forever.

Clay apologized to Jill, and he meant it—he really was sorry. He even offered to buy her a new mitt.

Complete the Making and Supporting Predictions Worksheet for the story.

Making and Supporting Predictions

Read the story below.

Curtain Time

The actors were in their costumes. They put the last touches on their make-up. From outside the dressing rooms, they could hear the audience talking and getting seated. Nerves were on edge. Would everyone remember their lines? Would the set, made mostly from painted cardboard and tape, hold up? Would the audience laugh at the funny events of the play?

Then the curtain went up, and the school play began. As the first scene progressed, the audience laughed and clapped, and no one forgot a line.

Complete the Making and Supporting Predictions Worksheet for the story.

© HMH Supplemental Publishers Inc. All rights reserved.

Name _____   Date _____

Making and Supporting Predictions Worksheet

Reading Title _____

Complete the Prediction Chart based on what you've read.

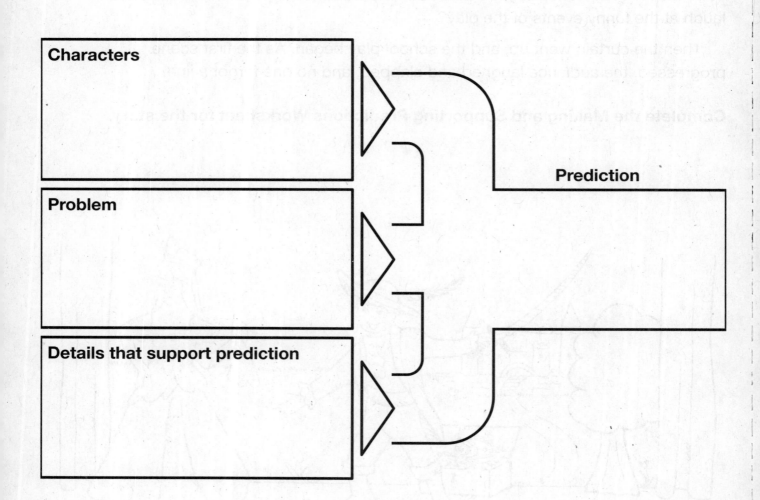

Characters

Problem

Details that support prediction

Prediction

Summary: Use the information in the Prediction Chart to write a summary of the reading selection.

_____

_____

Compare and Contrast

Presentation and Model

Strategy: Comparing and contrasting information that you need to summarize

When you compare, you look for how things are alike. When you contrast, you look for how things are different. Comparing and contrasting information helps you organize and make sense of what you read. Then you can write a clear, accurate summary.

Read the passage below.

Are you wondering whether a dog or a cat might be a good pet for you? Think carefully before you choose one of these pets. Both need to be fed and kept healthy with regular trips to the vet. Both will have to be trained to behave well, and both need affection.

However, when it comes to time, dogs need more than cats. A cat can stay by itself in the house all day, but a dog must go out for frequent walks. A cat can get exercise by playing inside with a little toy, but a dog needs to go outside to run and play fetch. A cat grooms itself, but a dog must be bathed often. A cat needs to be trained not to scratch where it shouldn't, but a dog needs a lot of training so that it won't jump and it will stay.

If you have just a little time to spend on a pet, consider getting a cat rather than a dog. If you have almost no time, how about some goldfish instead?

Complete the Venn Diagram based on what you've read.

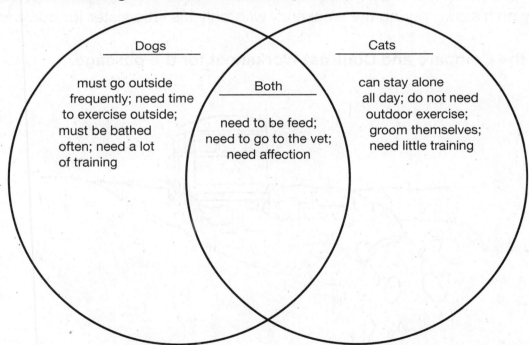

Dogs

must go outside frequently; need time to exercise outside; must be bathed often; need a lot of training

Both

need to be feed; need to go to the vet; need affection

Cats

can stay alone all day; do not need outdoor exercise; groom themselves; need little training

Summary: Use the information in the Venn Diagram to write a summary of the reading selection.

Dogs and cats can both be good pets, but cats take much less time than dogs.

People who have little time to spend with pets should choose a cat rather than a dog.

© HMH Supplemental Publishers Inc. All rights reserved. Summarizing Strategies Grade 5, SV 9781419099892

Compare and Contrast

Read the passage below.

Mondays and Saturdays

Carter can't decide which morning is better—Monday or Saturday. He likes both days because both bring their own kind of fun. But in most ways, these mornings are quite different.

On the one hand, on Saturdays Carter gets to sleep late, and when he gets up, there's no rush to get dressed and ready to leave. His parents often make a big, hot breakfast that day so that everyone has energy to do chores. The chores are the downside to Saturday morning. Carter knows when he wakes up that he'll have to do work around the farm before he can relax and do things he enjoys.

On the other hand, Carter has to be up early on Mondays. The school bus comes by the farm at 7 o'clock, and there's no one to drive Carter to school if he misses that bus. And breakfast on Monday morning is cold cereal and juice that must be gulped down. Still, Carter likes Monday morning because it means that he will soon see his friends again. Because Carter's family lives out in the country, he's usually on his own during the weekend, with only his little sister for company.

Complete the Compare and Contrast Worksheet for the passage.

Compare and Contrast

Read the passage below.

Summer or Winter

Which do you prefer: a long, warm summer day when the sun stays out late, or a cool winter evening with an early sunset?

In the summer, days are longer than in the winter. The angle of sunlight and the position of Earth in its orbit around the sun bring early dawns and late dusks. In some parts of the nation, the sun is out until 9:00 or later. Children can play lawn games until after bedtime. On the other hand, long days of sun mean higher temperatures. Sometimes temperatures are uncomfortable until well after sunset, and the short nights provide little time for the ground to cool off.

In winter, on the other hand, children who want to play outside must do so right after school is out. By 6 o'clock or even earlier, it will be dark. Some people find it harder to get up and get going in the morning, too, because dawn comes late. But winter skies can be clear and cool, and the stars are brilliant. And cool weather gives people a chance to wear their warm coats, play in fallen leaves and perhaps snow, and enjoy hot chocolate and spicy chili.

Both summer and winter days can be beautiful and full of fun.

Complete the Compare and Contrast Worksheet for the passage.

© HMH Supplemental Publishers Inc. All rights reserved.

Name _____   Date _____

Teacher's Toolbox

Compare and Contrast Worksheet

Reading Title _____

Complete the Venn Diagram based on what you've read.

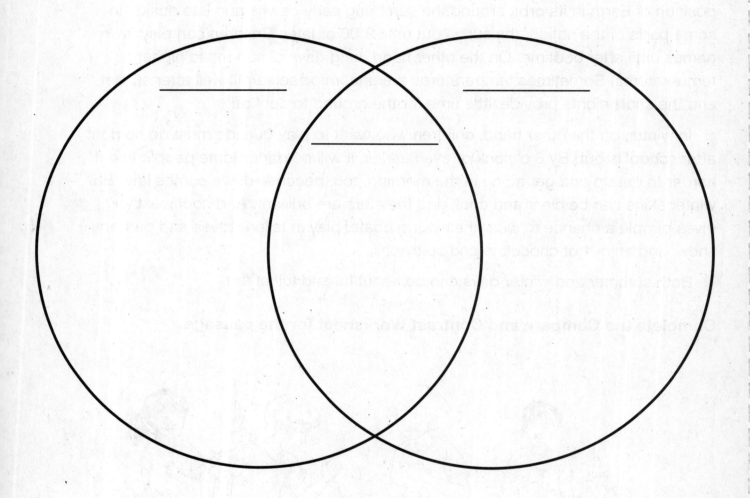

Summary: Use the information in the Venn Diagram to write a summary of the reading selection.

_____

_____

_____

© HMH Supplemental Publishers Inc. All rights reserved.
Summarizing Strategies Grade 5, SV 9781419099892

Summarizing Graphics

Presentation and Model

Strategy: Summarizing information that is presented in graphs, tables, and diagrams

Sometimes you will read information that is not presented in paragraphs. Information can also be included in graphs, charts and tables. You can use the skills you already know to summarize graphic information. Look for the main idea of the information along with supporting details.

One kind of graphic organization is the timeline. It organizes important events by date.

Study the timeline below.

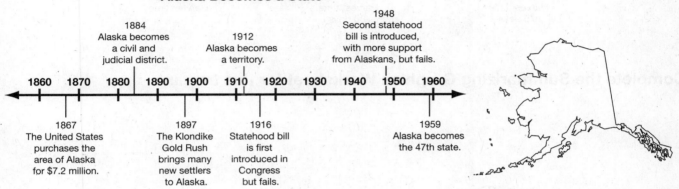

Alaska Becomes a State

1884 Alaska becomes a civil and judicial district.

1912 Alaska becomes a territory.

1948 Second statehood bill is introduced, with more support from Alaskans, but fails.

1860 1870 1880 1890 1900 1910 1920 1930 1940 1950 1960

1867 The United States purchases the area of Alaska for $7.2 million.

1897 The Klondike Gold Rush brings many new settlers to Alaska.

1916 Statehood bill is first introduced in Congress but fails.

1959 Alaska becomes the 47th state.

Complete the Graphics Table based on what you've read.

What is the graphic's title?	Alaska Becomes a State
What question does the graphic answer? (What is the graphic's main idea?)	important dates and events leading to Alaska becoming a state
What are the most important supporting details in the graphic?	1867, U.S. buys Alaska; 1912, Alaska becomes a territory; 1959, after two failed attempts, Alaska becomes a state

Summary: Use the information in the Graphics Table to write a summary of the timeline.

The United States purchased the land that is Alaska in 1867, but not until 1959, almost a century later, did Alaska become a state.

© HMH Supplemental Publishers Inc. All rights reserved.

Summarizing Graphics

Study the timeline below.

Central Texas Planting Guide

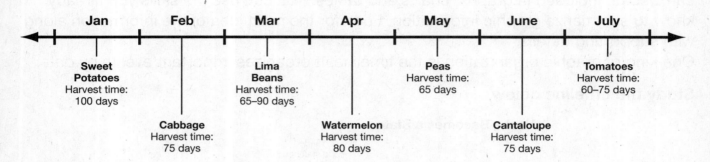

| Jan | Feb | Mar | Apr | May | June | July |

Sweet Potatoes
Harvest time: 100 days

Cabbage
Harvest time: 75 days

Lima Beans
Harvest time: 65–90 days

Watermelon
Harvest time: 80 days

Peas
Harvest time: 65 days

Cantaloupe
Harvest time: 75 days

Tomatoes
Harvest time: 60–75 days

Complete the Summarizing Graphics Worksheet for this timeline.

© HMH Supplemental Publishers Inc. All rights reserved.
Summarizing Strategies Grade 5, SV 9781419099892

Summarizing Graphics

Study the timeline below.

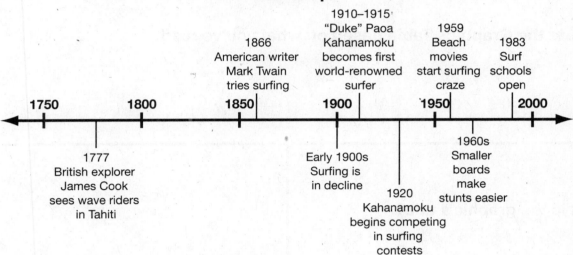

Surf's Up!

1866
American writer
Mark Twain
tries surfing

1910–1915
"Duke" Paoa
Kahanamoku
becomes first
world-renowned
surfer

1959
Beach
movies
start surfing
craze

1983
Surf
schools
open

1750   **1800**   **1850**   **1900**   **1950**   **2000**

1777
British explorer
James Cook
sees wave riders
in Tahiti

Early 1900s
Surfing is
in decline

1920
Kahanamoku
begins competing
in surfing
contests

1960s
Smaller
boards
make
stunts easier

Complete the Summarizing Graphics Worksheet for this timeline.

© HMH Supplemental Publishers Inc. All rights reserved.

Name _____   Date _____

Summarizing Graphics Worksheet

Graphic Title _____

Complete the Graphics Table based on what you've read.

What is the graphic's title?	
What question does the graphic answer? (What is the graphic's main idea?)	
What are the most important supporting details in the graphic?	

Summary: Use the information in the Graphics Table to write a summary of the graphic.

_____

_____

_____

© HMH Supplemental Publishers Inc. All rights reserved.
Summarizing Graphics
Summarizing Strategies Grade 5, SV 9781419099892

Character Traits

Presentation and Model

Strategy: Summarizing the traits of characters in stories you read

When you read a story, you have a chance to "meet" new people. The characters in the story are like people you get to know in real life. To get to know them, you must think about how they look and act, as well as what their personalities are like.

Read the story below.

"What's your name?" Peter asked his new next-door neighbor.

The boy pushed his brown hair to the left of his forehead with his right hand. "I'm Todd," he said. "Do you want to play some basketball?"

"I can't," Peter said. "I have to go to Dr. Donaldson's. Boy, I dread going to the dentist!"

Todd said. "That's our new dentist. I have an appointment today, too. I'll see you there!"

When Peter and his dad entered the dentist's office, there was Todd. "Wow! Have you seen the dentist already?" asked Peter, amazed.

"Yeah," said the boy, brushing his hair to the right with his left hand.

"How did you get here so fast?" asked Peter. "You were standing in your front yard when we left a few minutes ago."

The boy smiled broadly. "It's my superpower," he said. "I rub my right elbow, and I transport anywhere in town!"

When Peter came out of the dentist's office, there was Todd, sitting beside a boy who looked just like him. "I hear you met my brother, Thad, and that he's up to our old twin tricks!"

Complete the Character Trait Table based on what you've read.

Character(s): Todd and Thad		
Details about how character(s) looks	**Details about how character(s) acts**	**Details about the personality of the character(s)**
Both boys have brown hair, but they part it differently; they look alike because they are twins.	Todd is ready to make a new friend. Thad is ready to make a new friend, too, but he also enjoys tricking people.	Todd seems pleasant and friendly. Thad seems to have a good sense of humor and likes to be funny.

Summary: Use the information in the Character Trait Table to write a summary of the character(s).

Todd and Thad are twins. Both boys are friendly, and Thad seems to have a sense of humor. He likes to trick people.

Character Traits

Read the story below.

Words and Pictures

Alberto's teacher announced that the conference for young writers would take place the week after Thanksgiving. Alberto decided that he would like to go, so he brought in the registration form and fee. He then began thinking of an idea for his book. He remembered that his friend Allan had offered to draw pictures for his book. Alberto looked forward to working with Allan, so he asked Allan what he would like to draw.

"I can draw all kinds of animals," Allan said. So Alberto decided to write a fable about a camel that wanted to be a movie star.

Alberto worked on his story every day at school and at home. First, he wrote down his ideas for the plot, and slowly, the story unfolded. He revised it many times until it was just the way he wanted it. Then he and Allan discussed the pictures that would go on each page. When the book was done, the boys were very proud. They were ready to take their book to the conference.

Complete the Character Traits Worksheet for the story.

Character Traits

Read the story below.

Reading Contest

Ronnie walked up to the librarian at his elementary school and turned in two books. "That's two more, Mrs. Romanoli. How many have I read now?"

Mrs. Romanoli pulled out her notebook. "It looks like you are up to twenty-eight now. You have really blossomed, and I bet you win the reading contest."

Ronnie had read more books this year than ever before. In the past, Ronnie would only read if he had an assignment. He read because he wanted to get a good grade.

One day Ronnie made a discovery! His teacher suggested that he read a book about airplanes, his favorite hobby. He was so fascinated that he read other books about airplanes.

Now Ronnie reads about all kinds of hobbies. He has even found new hobbies through the books he has read.

Complete the Character Traits Worksheet for the story.

© HMH Supplemental Publishers Inc. All rights reserved.
Character Traits
Summarizing Strategies Grade 5, SV 9781419099892

Name _____ Date _____

Teacher's Toolbox

Character Traits Worksheet

Reading Title _____

Complete the Character Trait Table based on what you've read.

Character(s):		
Details about how character(s) looks	**Details about how character(s) acts**	**Details about the personality of the character(s)**

Summary: Use the information in the Character Trait Table to write a summary of the character.

_____

_____

_____

© HMH Supplemental Publishers Inc. All rights reserved.   Summarizing Strategies Grade 5, SV 9781419099892

Problems and Solutions

Presentation and Model

Strategy: Summarizing problems and solutions you read about

You will sometimes read paragraphs that talk about a problem and suggest solutions. Sometimes the problem and solution are simple. Sometimes, however, the problem is complicated, and many possible solutions are offered.

Read the article below.

Wetlands in the southeast are in danger. Over the years, wetlands have been drained so that homes and businesses can be built in their place. Other wetland areas have been polluted by run-off from manufacturing and agriculture. The animals that lived in the wetlands, including many kinds of birds, have lost their habitat.

For a long time, people have not understood why it is important to maintain the wetlands. They help the environment in several ways. First, they filter water to make it clean again. Second, they reduce the risk of flooding by trapping rainfall before it runs off. Also, they provide a natural barrier against storms. Wetlands often occur at the edge of the land and the ocean, so they are a buffer against storm-driven waves.

Now that people understand why wetlands are important, many are working to restore wetlands and even to make new ones. They are doing this by preventing the draining of more wetlands and building elsewhere instead. They are finding out how to stop pollution in the wetlands. And they are replanting wetland areas so that birds and animals will return.

Complete the Problem-Solution Frame based on what you've read.

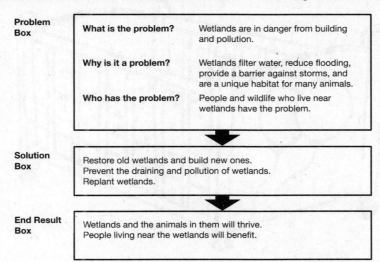

Problem Box

What is the problem?	Wetlands are in danger from building and pollution.
Why is it a problem?	Wetlands filter water, reduce flooding, provide a barrier against storms, and are a unique habitat for many animals.
Who has the problem?	People and wildlife who live near wetlands have the problem.

Solution Box

Restore old wetlands and build new ones.
Prevent the draining and pollution of wetlands.
Replant wetlands.

End Result Box

Wetlands and the animals in them will thrive.
People living near the wetlands will benefit.

Summary: Use the information in the Problem-Solution Frame to write a summary of the reading selection.

The problem is the loss of important wetlands to building and pollution, and the

solution is to protect existing wetlands and build new wetlands.

© HMH Supplemental Publishers Inc. All rights reserved.

Problems and Solutions

Read the story below.

Making Room for Baby

The Juarez family was very excited—they would soon have a new baby girl! But there was one little problem: Where would the new baby's room be? The family loved their home, with its shady porches and big back yard. And they liked their neighbors and the neighborhood, which was bordered by a large city park. They didn't want to move.

So Mom and Dad called the three brothers to a family meeting. Together, they decided to fix up the attic space for the baby. The attic, with its pointed roof, had been the brothers' playroom, but they were happy to give it up for their new little sister.

Everyone worked together to paint the room a soft yellow. Mom bought curtains with clouds and moons, and the boys got out the crib they all had used and cleaned it up. Soon, the little attic room was a perfect nook for a new baby.

Complete the Problems and Solutions Worksheet for the story.

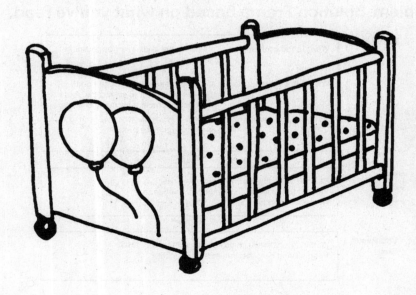

© HMH Supplemental Publishers Inc. All rights reserved.
Problems and Solutions
Summarizing Strategies Grade 5, SV 9781419099892

Problems and Solutions

Read the passage below.

Homework!

Sometimes it's easy to get your homework done, and sometimes it's not. You sit down to work, and it seems like a thousand things distract you. You know what's due in class the next day, but you just can't concentrate. Fortunately, there are solutions to your problem.

First, set aside a place just for homework. You may be thinking that your room is a good place to study, but it may be full of things to look at and do other than homework. Find a place that has fewer distractions. Perhaps the kitchen table would work.

Second, turn off your radio. Many students think that they can work and listen to music at the same time, but studies show that music distracts you from studying. (That goes for TVs, too.)

Third, make sure you have all your supplies so that you don't have to get up again and again.

Finally, have a plan. What do you need to study most? What is due first? Make a mental list, or a real one. Cross off each task as you complete it, and you will know that you are making progress!

Complete the Problems and Solutions Worksheet for the passage.

© HMH Supplemental Publishers Inc. All rights reserved.

Name _____   Date _____

Teacher's Toolbox

Problems and Solutions Worksheet

Reading Title _____

Complete the Problem-Solution Frame based on what you've read.

Problem Box

> **What is the problem?**
>
> **Why is it a problem?**
>
> **Who has the problem?**

Solution Box

End Result Box

Summary: Use the information in the Problem-Solution Frame to write a summary of the reading selection.

_____

_____

_____

www.harcourtschoolsupply.com
© HMH Supplemental Publishers Inc. All rights reserved.

Problems and Solutions
Summarizing Strategies Grade 5, SV 9781419099892

Analyzing Characters

Presentation and Model

Strategy: Summarizing characters' actions and motivations

The way characters act, and the things they think and say can help explain a story. When you analyze characters, you gather information to write a summary of their behavior.

Read the story below.

Tony got up early Tuesday morning, ate breakfast, put on his new shoes, and started walking to school. The sun was out, and the breeze was pleasant. "This is going to be a great day!" he thought.

Halfway to school, Tony realized that he had forgotten his homework. He was so worried about what his teacher would say that he didn't see the mud puddle until he had stepped in it. "Well, it's no big deal," he thought. "I'll bring the work tomorrow and clean my shoes later."

At school, Tony's best friend was angry because Tony forgot to stop by his house on the way to school. Then Tony heard that basketball practice, his favorite part of the day, was cancelled. "What else can go wrong?" he thought.

When lunchtime arrived, Tony was not at all surprised to find that he had forgotten his lunch. He had no money to buy one, either. "I guess," he thought, "that I'd better not decide how great the day will be until I see how it goes!"

Complete the Character Profile based on what you've read.

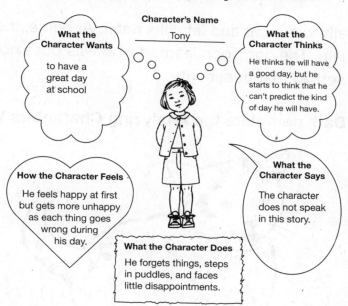

Character's Name
Tony

What the Character Wants
to have a great day at school

What the Character Thinks
He thinks he will have a good day, but he starts to think that he can't predict the kind of day he will have.

How the Character Feels
He feels happy at first but gets more unhappy as each thing goes wrong during his day.

What the Character Says
The character does not speak in this story.

What the Character Does
He forgets things, steps in puddles, and faces little disappointments.

Summary: Use the information in the Character Profile to write a summary of the character.

Tony is a carefree boy, but when things keep going wrong, he begins to wonder
whether he has much control over his day.

© HMH Supplemental Publishers Inc. All rights reserved.
Summarizing Strategies Grade 5, SV 9781419099892

Analyzing Characters

Read the story below.

A Kitten for Julie

The Alister family was having a picnic in the park. As they were cleaning up to go home, Julie, the youngest child, said, "Hey! Did you hear that?"

Everyone quieted down to listen, and soon they heard a squeaky meowing sound. "It sounds like a cat!" said Julie. "We have to find it—maybe it's a stray."

Moving calmly so that the cat would not be frightened away, Julie's parents began to look for the cat. "Here it is," Dad said, pointing under a bush. "It's just a kitten."

The kitten was white, though its fur was dirty and matted. "It's a fighter," Dad said. "Look how it's walking right up to us—it's not afraid at all. It looks like it expects a ride home."

"Oh, Dad, Mom, can we keep it?" Julie asked. "It needs a home!"

Dad hesitated. He wasn't sure whether the family had time for another pet. Still, this kitten looked healthy and alert, and Dad could see how much Julie wanted to keep it.

The kitten rode quietly in the car and let Julie pet it. At home, the Alisters' dog was waiting to greet them. The dog soon learned who was boss now. One swat of the feisty kitten's paw settled that question!

For the character of Dad, complete the Analyzing Characters Worksheet for the story.

© HMH Supplemental Publishers Inc. All rights reserved.

Summarizing Strategies Grade 5, SV 9781419099892

Analyzing Characters

Read the story below.

The White Blouse

"Mom!" Jocelyn complained. "I've outgrown my white blouse, and I need one for the school debate next week." Jocelyn looked at herself in the mirror. The crisp white blouse she had on was stretched across her shoulders, and the sleeves were much too short.

"I can't believe how quickly you're growing," said her mother, coming into the room. "We just bought you that blouse, it seems! Well, it's almost like new, so your little sister will get some use out of it."

"But what about me?" Jocelyn complained. "I can't participate in the debate without a white shirt!"

"Then let's shop," Mom said, grabbing her keys.

Jocelyn and her mother spent three hours combing through racks of clothes at the mall. Nothing fit quite right. Nothing looked quite right. Finally, Jocelyn became frustrated and snapped, "You're not helping me at all, Mom!"

Right away, Jocelyn felt bad. She saw her mother's face fall. She put an arm around her mother's shoulder. "I'm so sorry," she said. "You're spending your day off shopping for something you don't even need, and you're doing it all for me."

"That's okay," Mom said. "Here's a new plan. Let's go home, make a cup of tea, and shop for a blouse online."

Mother and daughter were both smiling as they walked to the parking lot.

For the character of Jocelyn, complete the Analyzing Characters Worksheet for the story.

Name _____ Date _____

Analyzing Characters Worksheet

Reading Title _____

Complete the Character Profile based on what you've read.

Character's Name

_____

What the Character Wants

What the Character Thinks

How the Character Feels

What the Character Says

What the Character Does

Summary: Use the information in the Character Profile to write a summary of the character.

_____

_____

_____

Cause and Effect

Presentation and Model

Strategy: Identifying and summarizing causes and effects

A cause is an event than makes another event happen. The effect is the next event that happens as a result of the cause. You see causes and effects around you every day:

Cause: You eat lunch. ——→ **Effect:** You are no longer hungry.

Cause: You forget your jacket. ——→ **Effect:** You get cold walking to school.

Read the story below.

The fox followed the rabbit's tracks, trotting persistently for over an hour. He was tired, cold, and hungry. The deep new snowfall made finding food very hard. So the fox had been tempted to try other ways to get food. Just yesterday, a farmer chased him away from the chickens.

The fox paused, sniffing the ground and the air. At last, he turned back and retraced his steps, but it was no use. He lost the rabbit's trail in the undergrowth of the woods. He would likely go hungry for another day unless he could find new prey.

Complete the Cause and Effect Chart based on what you've read.

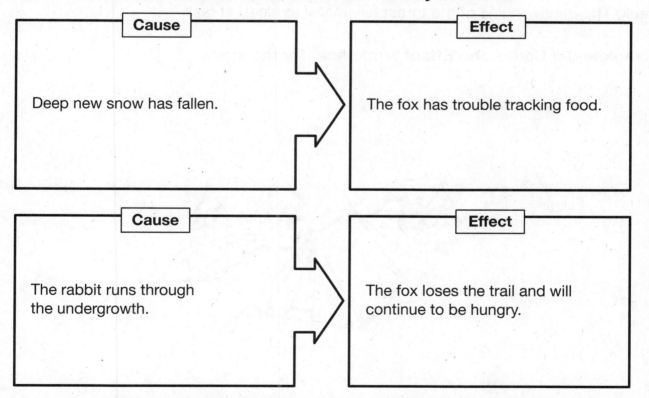

Cause	Effect
Deep new snow has fallen.	The fox has trouble tracking food.
The rabbit runs through the undergrowth.	The fox loses the trail and will continue to be hungry.

Summary: Use the information in the Cause and Effect Chart to write a summary of the reading selection.

Snowy winter weather makes it hard for the fox to follow the rabbit's tracks. The fox will continue to be hungry.

© HMH Supplemental Publishers Inc. All rights reserved.

Cause and Effect
Summarizing Strategies Grade 5, SV 9781419099892

Cause and Effect

Read the story below.

The Great Outdoors

Mai picked out what looked like a smooth patch of ground to pitch her tent. She put her pack inside and spread out her sleeping bag. After a long day hiking, she was sure she'd sleep soundly.

But after Mai snuggled into the bag, she had a hard time falling asleep. The patch of ground that had looked so smooth seemed to have a hundred hard little rocks on it. Mai felt rocks under her shoulders, back, and legs. She shifted around, trying to find the smoothest place to sleep. "I'll have to move my tent tomorrow," she thought.

Finally, Mai felt comfortable enough to sleep, but still, she lay awake in the tent. She began to listen to the night's sounds. Insects whirred. Wind brushed the branches of the trees. From the foot of the hill came the soothing sounds of the creek. The gentle music of the forest lulled Mai to sleep at last.

Complete the Cause and Effect Worksheet for the story.

© HMH Supplemental Publishers Inc. All rights reserved.

Cause and Effect

Read the story below.

Scary Sleepover

When Charlotte arrived to sleep over at her friend Shanna's house, Shanna greeted her excitedly. "Guess what?" she said. "My parents say we can stay up and watch a scary movie on TV!"

"Great!" said Charlotte, as she thought unhappily about the last time she had watched a scary movie.

The girls made a big bowl of popcorn and settled in to watch the movie. Then they climbed into sleeping bags on the den floor and shut off the light.

"Shanna," Charlotte said after a few minutes, "are you scared? I can't get the monsters from the movie out of my head."

"Yeah, they were pretty scary. I'm having trouble falling asleep."

Charlotte said nothing for a while. She didn't want to admit to being afraid to go to sleep. Then Shanna got up. "I'm going to get a drink of water from the kitchen," she explained. When she came back, she didn't turn out the kitchen light. From the door of the kitchen, soft light spilled into part of the den.

"No monsters here!" thought Charlotte happily as she fell asleep at last.

Complete the Cause and Effect Worksheet for the story.

© HMH Supplemental Publishers Inc. All rights reserved.

Summarizing Strategies Grade 5, SV 9781419099892

Name _____ Date _____

Cause and Effect Worksheet

Reading Title _____

Complete the Cause and Effect Chart based on what you've read.

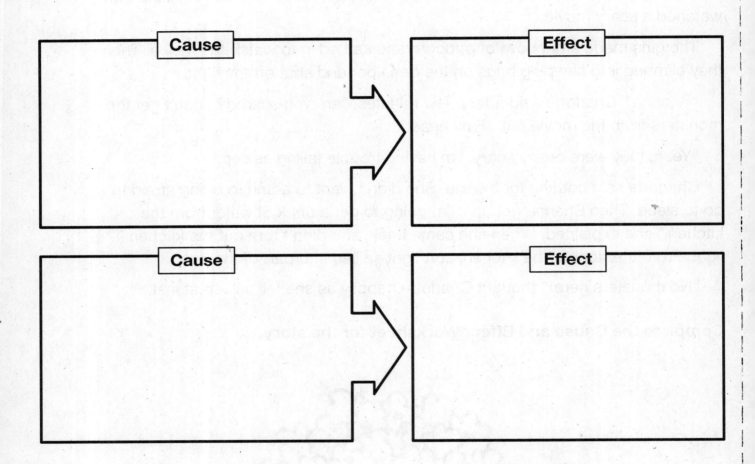

Cause	Effect

Cause	Effect

Summary: Use the information in the Cause and Effect Chart to write a summary of the reading selection.

_____

_____

_____

www.harcourtschoolsupply.com
© HMH Supplemental Publishers Inc. All rights reserved.

Cause and Effect
Summarizing Strategies Grade 5, SV 9781419099892

Cause and Multiple Effects

Presentation and Model

Strategy: Summarizing causal relationships that involve more than one effect

Causal relationships are the connections between events that happen. Sometimes a single cause leads to a single effect. Sometimes, however, a single cause may have many effects. You must read carefully to identify each part of the causal relationship.

Read the story below.

On the first day of summer vacation, Greta tripped on a rug and broke her ankle. Getting the ankle treated hurt, but not as much as knowing how much fun she would miss out on because she had to wear a clunky cast. Greta had big plans: two weeks at a summer camp, where she would learn to ride a horse, and many days spent splashing in the city pool. Now she would have to cancel those plans.

As she sat moping in her room, thinking of all the fun she couldn't have, Greta heard a knock on the door. It was her grandmother, and she was holding some brochures.

"Dear, I'm so sorry about your ankle," said Grandmother. "But I have an idea about how you can have fun this summer despite the cast." She held out a colorful brochure. "Let's take some classes together. I've always wanted to try pottery, and here's a class on watercolor, and another on learning to make beads for jewelry. What do you think?"

Greta smiled. Maybe this summer wouldn't be as bad as she had thought.

Complete the Cause with Multiple Effects Diagram based on what you've read.

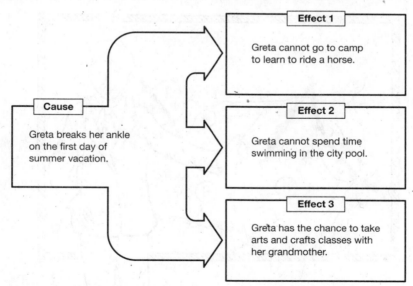

Cause

Greta breaks her ankle on the first day of summer vacation.

Effect 1

Greta cannot go to camp to learn to ride a horse.

Effect 2

Greta cannot spend time swimming in the city pool.

Effect 3

Greta has the chance to take arts and crafts classes with her grandmother.

Summary: Use the information in the Cause with Multiple Effects Diagram to write a summary of the reading selection.

<u>An injury threatens to spoil a girl's summer fun, but her grandmother comes up with</u>

<u>new fun things to do.</u>

Cause and Multiple Effects

Read the article below.

Rain, Rain, Come Today

What happens when too little rain falls? You may not think much about rainfall amounts, but many people watch the weather closely, especially during the summer.

Farmers, for instance, know that if it rains too little during the summer growing season, their crops will suffer. The crops need rain to thrive, and farmers will have to spend extra money to irrigate their fields if the weather is dry.

People who study the weather pay close attention to rainfall amounts, too. They know that dry summer days lead to hotter days later on. Rain cools the ground. Without rain, the ground gets hard and holds the heat better through the night.

City managers watch the summer skies closely, too. Rain fills up lakes and reservoirs from which cities get their water. In a dry summer, these water supplies get used up faster, and cities may have to ration water.

Complete the Cause and Multiple Effects Worksheet for the article.

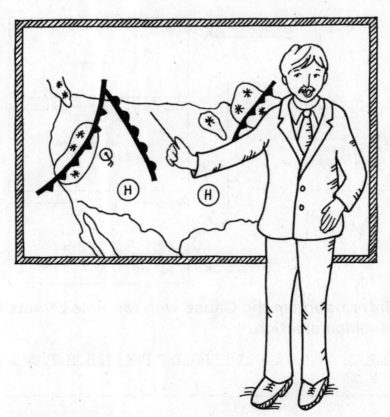

© HMH Supplemental Publishers Inc. All rights reserved.

Cause and Multiple Effects

Read the story below.

Diana's First Day

Diana's stomach did flip-flops as the bus pulled up to her new school. She didn't know anyone, and her nervousness was obvious. Diana's teacher could see how scared Diana was, so she asked a friendly student, Tia, to help Diana through her first day.

Tia and Diana liked each other immediately, and just knowing someone's name made Diana feel better. Tia introduced Diana to other students and helped her find her way to classrooms. Most importantly, Tia invited Diana to sit with her and her friends at lunch.

Diana had been dreading lunchtime most of all. But instead of feeling sad and missing friends at her old school, Diana was happy and excited to be meeting new friends.

The first day at her new school was a success for Diana, and all because her teacher had introduced her to Tia.

Complete the Cause and Multiple Effects Worksheet for the story.

Name _____ Date _____

Teacher's Toolbox

Cause and Multiple Effects Worksheet

Reading Title _____

Complete the Cause with Multiple Effects Diagram based on what you've read.

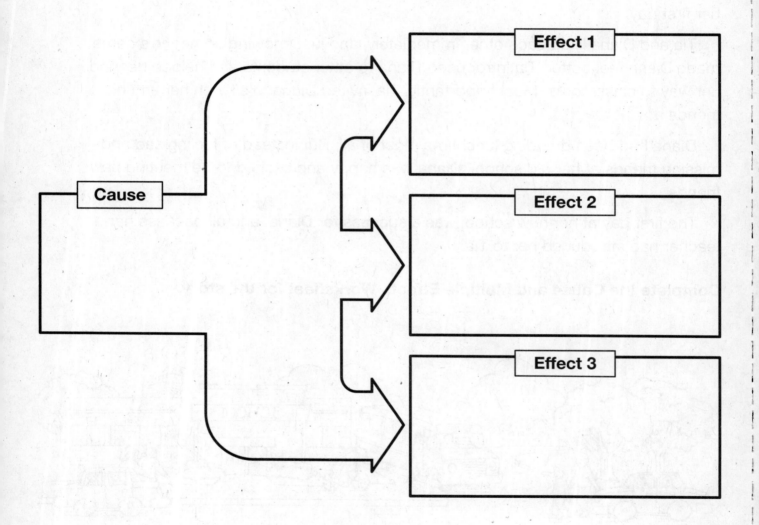

Cause

Effect 1

Effect 2

Effect 3

Summary: Use the information in the Cause with Multiple Effects Diagram to write a summary of the reading selection.

_____

_____

_____

© HMH Supplemental Publishers Inc. All rights reserved.
Cause and Multiple Effects
Summarizing Strategies Grade 5, SV 9781419099892

Fact and Opinion

Presentation and Model

Strategy: Distinguishing between facts and opinions in what you read

A fact is a piece of information that can be proven or confirmed. For example, a word's meaning is a fact. You can check it in a dictionary. The height of a mountain is a fact. An opinion is what someone thinks based on facts. The same fact can lead to different opinions. Think about a mountain again. One person might say a 7,000-foot mountain is "really tall." Another person might say, "No, 14,000 feet is tall—this mountain is small." The two people have formed different opinions based on the same fact.

Read the passage below.

What has fur and wings, flies at night, and sleeps upside down during the day? A bat, of course! Bats are the only flying mammals. Other mammals, such as flying squirrels, may glide, but bats, like birds, actually fly.

Bats live in large groups called colonies. During the warmer months, the entire colony takes flight at dusk. Seeing hundreds or thousands of bats on the wing is exciting! The bats fly in swarms from their upside-down perches in search of insects. One bat can eat up to 1,000 disgusting insects in an hour.

Bat colonies may be found in caves, but bats also live under bridges right in the middle of cities. Tourists may go watch the bat flight during the evening. However, some people dislike bats. They believe that bats bite people and are dangerous. Actually, bats are beneficial to the environment.

Complete the Fact-Opinion Table based on what you've read.

Facts	Opinions
Bats are mammals with fur and wings.	It is exciting to see hundreds or thousands of bats in flight.
Bats are the only flying mammals.	The insects bats eat are disgusting.
Bats live in colonies in caves or under bridges.	Bats bite people and are dangerous.
Bats sleep upside down.	
Bats eat up to 1,000 insects an hour.	
Bats fly out to eat at dusk during warm months.	
Tourists watch bat flights.	
Bats are beneficial to the environment.	

Summary: Use the information in the Fact-Opinion Table to write a summary of the facts from the reading selection.

Bats are very special mammals. They are the only mammals that can fly. Many live in caves and under bridges. They help the environment by eating thousands of bugs.

© HMH Supplemental Publishers Inc. All rights reserved.

Fact and Opinion

Read the passage below.

Tippy the Busy Puppy

Puppies require a lot of care. Joy recently got a new puppy. Tippy is a very busy puppy, and Joy works hard to keep up with him. Tippy wakes Joy up early and yips until she gets his breakfast. What an annoying puppy! After he eats, Tippy barks politely to go outside. Once Joy lets him out, he has much to do. He has to check every corner of the yard, to make sure that everything is in order. He sometimes digs holes by the fence. Joy has to fill them in again.

Despite the work, having a puppy is worth the trouble. Tippy plays with Joy, chasing balls and fetching them back to her. A ball covered with mud and dog slobber is no fun to throw! Tippy also helps the family. He barks when anyone approaches the door. But most of all, Tippy makes Joy laugh. It's so fun to watch him chase his tail!

Complete the Fact and Opinion Worksheet for the passage.

Fact and Opinion

Read the passage below.

When Dinosaurs Roamed

Although it is hard to imagine, dinosaurs once roamed our world in great numbers. We know about the great diversity of dinosaurs from fossilized bones dug out of the ground and from footprints and other imprints in stone. The work of fossil hunters can be dangerous and tiring, but it is also a lot of fun. We know that dinosaurs ranged from the size of roosters to the size of houses. The little ones must have been cute!

Studying the fossilized teeth of dinosaurs tells us that some ate plants, while others ate meat, much like animals of today. There were dinosaurs that lived on land, those that swam the seas, and even some that glided on air.

It's a good thing that all the dinosaurs are now extinct. It would be strange to share our world with them today. After all, even their bones are scary!

Complete the Fact and Opinion Worksheet for the passage.

© HMH Supplemental Publishers Inc. All rights reserved.
Summarizing Strategies Grade 5, SV 9781419099892

Name_____ Date _____

Fact and Opinion Worksheet

Reading Title _____

Complete the Fact-Opinion Table based on what you've read.

Facts	Opinions

Summary: Use the information in the Fact-Opinion Table to write a summary of the facts from the reading selection.

_____

_____

_____

© HMH Supplemental Publishers Inc. All rights reserved.
Summarizing Strategies Grade 5, SV 9781419099892

Author's Purpose

Presentation and Model

Strategy: Determining the author's purpose in writing a nonfiction or fiction selection

Why do authors write? Sometimes they want to inform readers. Sometimes they hope to entertain readers. They may want to persuade readers to think or act a certain way. Often, writers combine these purposes. An article could inform you about ways to recycle and persuade you to recycle more of your trash, for example.

Ask these questions to decide the author's purpose:

- Have I learned anything from this selection? (to inform)
- Did I laugh or smile at anything in this selection? (to entertain)
- Have I changed my mind about something after reading this selection? (to persuade)
- Will I act differently after reading this selection? (to persuade)

Read the passage below.

Cellulose is the woody part of plants that gives them stiffness. Without cellulose, people would be without thousands of articles they use every day. Cotton fibers, coco matting, and manila rope are largely cellulose. Wood, too, is mostly cellulose, as is the paper that is made from wood. Cellulose is also used to manufacture some plastics.

Imagine waking up to a world without products made from cellulose: Your favorite T-shirt and jeans no longer exist. What will you wear to school? You need to take notes from a textbook, but where are the pages of the book and your writing paper? You wouldn't have a desk to work at, either. These examples are humorous, but life without cellulose would not be funny!

Complete the Author's Purpose Chart based on what you've read.

To Inform	To Entertain
Did I learn something as I read? _✓_ Yes ___ No	Did I smile or laugh as I read? _✓_ Yes ___ No
To Persuade Me to Think Did the reading ask me to change what I think about something? ___ Yes _✓_ No	**To Persuade Me to Act** Did the reading ask me to do something or change my behavior? ___ Yes _✓_ No

Summary: Use the information in the Author's Purpose Chart to write a summary of the reading selection.

The author gave information about cellulose. The description of a world without

products made from cellulose was entertaining.

Author's Purpose

Read the article below.

That's a Real Brand Name

Cattle raisers use brands to mark their cattle. Cattle roam a long way as they graze. They can get mixed with cattle from another ranch. The custom of marking calves with the owner's brand is common. Cowhands separate the calves from the herd, rope them, and brand them. Then the calves return to their mothers.

Some people wonder whether the practice of branding should end. They point out that brands are burned into a calf's hide. These people argue that there are less painful ways to mark cattle for later identification, such as tagging their ears. Many cattle raisers do, in fact, tag the ear. But others claim that ear tags can be removed. Theft of livestock, sometimes called *rustling,* is a problem today just as it was in the days of the cattle drive. Without a permanent brand, they question how people will be able to identify their herds beyond a doubt.

Complete the Author's Purpose Worksheet for the article.

© HMH Supplemental Publishers Inc. All rights reserved.
Author's Purpose
Summarizing Strategies Grade 5, SV 9781419099892

Author's Purpose

Read the brochure below.

Park Clean-Up Saturday!
Pleasant River Park Needs Your Help!

Pleasant River Park is the jewel of our city—a green, shady place where people jog, walk their dogs, picnic, and fish. But the park needs to be cleaned up. Recent flooding left branches, trash, and other debris all over the park. Join us for Park Clean-Up Saturday, and help restore our park!

Date: Saturday, September 23
Time: 8 A.M. until 3 P.M.
Bring: Work gloves, rakes, shovels

The city will provide healthy snacks and water to all volunteers. If we work together, our park will be clean by late afternoon!

Complete the Author's Purpose Worksheet for this brochure.

© HMH Supplemental Publishers Inc. All rights reserved.
Summarizing Strategies Grade 5, SV 9781419099892

Name _____ Date _____

Author's Purpose Worksheet

Reading Title _____

Complete the Author's Purpose Chart based on what you've read.

To Inform Did I learn something as I read? _____ Yes _____ No	**To Entertain** Did I smile or laugh as I read? _____ Yes _____ No
To Persuade Me to Think Did the reading ask me to change what I think about something? _____ Yes _____ No	**To Persuade Me to Act** Did the reading ask me to do something or change my behavior? _____ Yes _____ No

Summary: Use the information in the Author's Purpose Chart to write a summary of the reading selection.

_____

_____

_____

© HMH Supplemental Publishers Inc. All rights reserved.
Summarizing Strategies Grade 5, SV 9781419099892

Drawing Conclusions

Presentation and Model

Strategy: Drawing conclusions from what you read

When you draw conclusions, you make a judgment based on information you read and what you already know. However, you don't want to "jump to conclusions," or draw a conclusion that is not supported by what you read. Instead, look for clear information in the reading, which leads to the judgment you make.

Read the article below.

Dogs are special animals that have many kinds of jobs. Dogs can be trained to help blind and deaf people live more independently. They serve as eyes or ears for disabled people. Some dogs have even been trained to act as a person's hands. They can be trained to get things that someone is unable to reach.

Other dogs have special talents for tracking people and have been used to find missing people. An article of the person's clothing gives the dog the scent, and it can then follow the path the person has taken.

Some dogs are good guard dogs. They protect people, herds of animals, possessions, and property.

Many dogs serve yet another special function: They provide people with companionship. For most dog owners, a dog is not just a pet. It is a friend or even a member of the family.

Complete the Conclusion Trains based on what you've read.

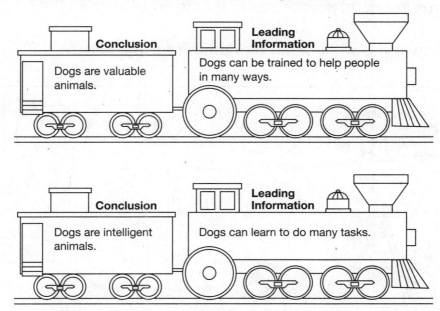

Conclusion
Dogs are valuable animals.

Leading Information
Dogs can be trained to help people in many ways.

Conclusion
Dogs are intelligent animals.

Leading Information
Dogs can learn to do many tasks.

Summary: Use the information in the Conclusion Trains to write a summary of the reading selection.

Dogs are valuable, intelligent animals that can be trained to help people in many

different ways.

© HMH Supplemental Publishers Inc. All rights reserved.
Summarizing Strategies Grade 5, SV 9781419099892

Drawing Conclusions

Read the article below.

Seasons in the Park

In spring, the city park is bright with new grass and flowers. In the mornings, a little frost still glistens on the swing set, but children are eager to play after the long winter. Children scan the reeds on the edge of the lake for duck nests and count eggs.

In summer, the park is richly green. Rushes and reeds grow thick by the lake, hiding the newly-hatched ducklings until they are ready to try the water. Now the black strap seats of the swings soak up the sun, and children are careful not to let them touch bare skin.

Fall brings color to the park. The leaves turn gold and red, just as they've done for many years, and children gather them to press between books. The swings creak in the wind, tired after months of use. The ducks, sensing the coming of winter, are getting ready to fly.

But in winter—in winter the park is a lonely place. Few people visit, because cold winds blow off the lake. The swings are icy and unused. Still, some people come, with children in tow, to scatter seeds for the wintering birds.

Complete the Drawing Conclusions Worksheet for the article.

Drawing Conclusions

Read the story below.

Maria Bakes

Maria decided to make a cake. She got out all the ingredients and heated the oven. As she was mixing the ingredients, her best friend called.

"Maria!" Gail said. "You won't believe what I just heard!" Gail began to tell about a friend who was moving out of state. But Maria kept mixing as she listened.

Then she said, "Hang on a minute, Gail. I need to put a cake in the oven." She set the phone down, poured the batter into round pans, and placed them in the oven. Then she picked up the phone. "Okay, go on with your story!" she said, walking into the den to relax on the sofa.

One topic led to another as the friends chatted for a while. Maria had the feeling that she'd forgotten something, but she was having too good a time talking to think much about it.

That is, until she smelled something.

"Oh, no—my cake!" Maria suddenly cried, interrupting Gail. She dropped the phone and hurried to the kitchen. In her haste, she did not forget to be careful. She put on oven mitts and pulled out the steaming pans, setting them on racks to cool.

"So is your cake burned?" Gail asked when Maria returned to the phone.

"Just a little," Maria said. "Now, what were you saying?"

Complete the Drawing Conclusions Worksheet for the story.

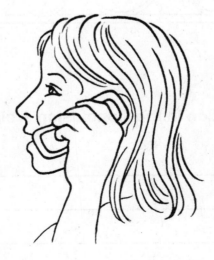

© HMH Supplemental Publishers Inc. All rights reserved.

Name _____   Date _____

Drawing Conclusions Worksheet

Story Title _____

Complete the Conclusion Trains based on what you've read.

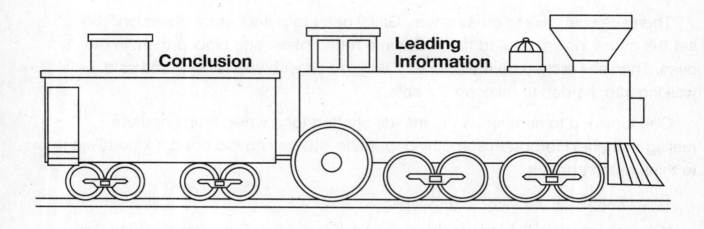

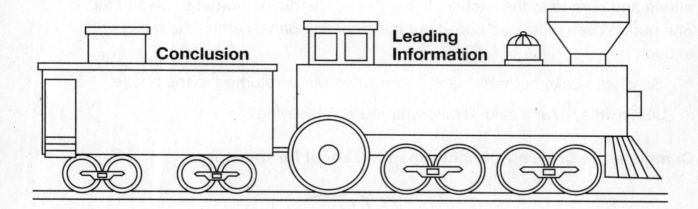

Summary: Use the information in the Conclusion Trains to write a summary of the reading selection.

_____

_____

Making Inferences

Presentation and Model

Strategy: Making inferences based on what you read

Authors usually do not explain every idea in detail. Instead, they provide enough information to help readers make inferences, or logical guesses. You add one idea to another to understand how they work together, almost the same way you add two numbers to come up with a new number.

Read the article below.

Aquifers are important geological formations. Aquifers are layers of porous rock, rock filled with holes large and small. These rock layers lie below the soil. When rain falls, some runs off into rivers and lakes. Some evaporates to form new clouds. But some rain filters through the soil and then through layers of porous rock. This rain is called groundwater. It seeps through porous rock, seeking reservoirs under the ground.

Water in aquifers is clean because it has been filtered through soil and rock. In low-lying areas, it may flow from the ground as springs or streams. Cities built above aquifers draw on the reserve of water beneath them. For instance, San Antonio, Texas, sits above the important, vast Edwards Aquifer.

Unfortunately, the water in aquifers can become polluted. Spilt motor oil, run-off from heavily fertilized lawns, and other chemicals can leak into an aquifer. Then its water is no longer clean and fit for use.

Complete the Add Up for Inference graphic based on what you've read.

> **First Clue:**
>
> Water in aquifers is used by many cities.

+

> **Second Clue:**
>
> Water in aquifers can become polluted by chemicals.

> **Inference:**
>
> Cities must try to prevent chemicals from getting into the aquifers they depend on for water.

Summary: Use the information in the Add Up for Inference graphic to write a summary of the reading selection.

Aquifers are important sources of water for many cities, and they must be protected from pollution.

© HMH Supplemental Publishers Inc. All rights reserved.
Summarizing Strategies Grade 5, SV 9781419099892

Making Inferences

Prairie Dogs

Have you ever visited a prairie dog town? If you have, you know that prairie dogs live in burrows underground. In fact, prairie dogs are actually burrowing squirrels. People call them prairie dogs because of the range of barks, yips, snarls, and growls they use to communicate.

Even a small prairie dog town can have a hundred or more inhabitants. Some time ago, however, much larger towns were common across the plains. A colony in Texas, which no longer exists, once covered more than 25,000 square miles and was home to an estimated 400 million prairie dogs!

Prairie dog numbers have decreased in recent decades because the animals are regarded as pests. Disease has reduced some colonies as well. But today, the role of the prairie dog in keeping the prairie habitat healthy is better understood. Perhaps prairie dogs will soon be thought of not as pests but as preservers of the prairie.

Complete the Making Inferences Worksheet for the article.

Making Inferences

Read the brochure below.

Mateo's Lawn Service

Do you need someone to look after your lawn this summer?

Meet your neighbor Mateo!

I'm a fifth grader at Pearl Elementary, and I can help you take care of your lawn.

I have been helping my dad care for our lawn at 2211 Prindle Street for two years.

Drive by and take a look at the results!

I can provide these services:

Lawn mowing
Watering
Weeding
Trimming
Planting
Sweeping and Raking

My rates are reasonable! So call today to set up your lawn care schedule!

Complete the Making Inferences Worksheet for the brochure.

© HMH Supplemental Publishers Inc. All rights reserved.
Summarizing Strategies Grade 5, SV 9781419099892

Name _____ Date _____

Making Inferences Worksheet

Reading Title _____

Complete the Add Up for Inference graphic based on what you've read.

First Clue:

+

Second Clue:

Inference:

Summary: Use the information in the Add Up for Inference graphic to write a summary of the reading selection.

_____

_____

_____

© HMH Supplemental Publishers Inc. All rights reserved.
Making Inferences
Summarizing Strategies Grade 5, SV 9781419099892

Forming Generalizations

Presentation and Model

Strategy: Forming sound generalizations based on what you read

When you read specific information about a topic and then come up with a broader statement about that topic, you are forming a generalization.

Specific Fact: Everyone you see is carrying an umbrella.

Generalization: People must be expecting rain.

Read the article below.

The guitar seems like a very modern instrument. However, the guitar's history stretches back four centuries.

The first guitars were probably built in Spain in the early sixteenth century. These early guitars had only four strings; the fifth and sixth strings were added over a century later. They were also deeper than today's guitars and made of heavier wood.

In the twentieth century, inventors worked to change guitars in several ways. Acoustic (non-electric) guitars were hard to hear in the popular big band music of the 1940s. So inventors began to think of ways to electrify the guitar. Two inventors were especially important at this time. Les Paul pioneered the solid body electric guitar, and Leo Fender made the solid body easier to manufacture.

By the 1950s many people could buy electric guitars. The popularity of this instrument changed the music scene forever.

Complete the Generalization Pyramid based on what you've read.

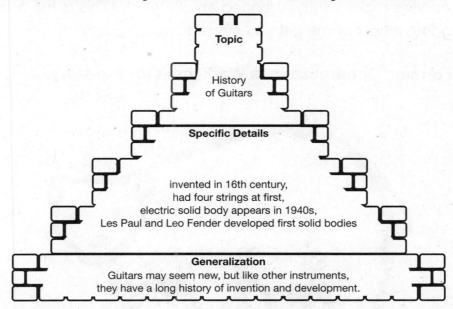

Topic

History of Guitars

Specific Details

invented in 16th century,
had four strings at first,
electric solid body appears in 1940s,
Les Paul and Leo Fender developed first solid bodies

Generalization
Guitars may seem new, but like other instruments,
they have a long history of invention and development.

Summary: Use the information in the Generalization Pyramid to write a summary of the reading selection.

Guitars were invented in Spain during the 16th century. Over the centuries, many new developments have led to the guitars we know today.

© HMH Supplemental Publishers Inc. All rights reserved.

Forming Generalizations

Read the story below.

Learning to Carve Wood

Hector knew that his father's birthday was coming up in a month. He was planning to make him a very special gift. His idea was to make a woodcarving of a bear, the mascot of his dad's favorite team.

Hector found a piece of wood in his yard that was about the size that he wanted to use. He started trying to carve. Hector was having a hard time because the wood seemed very hard. He was also having trouble getting small details using his knife. Hector thought about his friend Mr. McDorman, and how easy he made woodworking look. "I'll go talk to him," Hector thought.

Mr. McDorman looked at Hector's work and right away was able to offer some advice. "You're using mesquite wood. That is much too hard for what you are doing. Here, use this piece of pine." Things were working better already.

When Hector started to try to put details on his carving, Mr. McDorman stopped him. "You are going to have a hard time making details with that knife. Let's look over here." He opened a drawer and Hector looked inside. There sat a dozen different carving tools, neatly arranged and labeled. "This is the one you want for shaping the nose. Let me get you started."

Complete the Forming Generalizations Worksheet for the story.

© HMH Supplemental Publishers Inc. All rights reserved.
Summarizing Strategies Grade 5, SV 9781419099892

Forming Generalizations

Read the story below.

Birds in the Snow

Lily looked out the kitchen window. A light snow had fallen and then mixed with dirt to make a muddy mess. She sighed. "No outside play today," she thought.

"Mom, why does winter have to last so long?" she griped.

Her mother turned from her work. "It won't last forever," she said. "And you're warm and dry inside the house, so you have something to be grateful for. Look at the birds—they're probably shivering despite their puffed-up feathers."

Lily watched the birds peck at the snow. She did feel grateful for a cozy house and for the toast and honey she was eating for breakfast. She also felt a little guilty for griping—she definitely had an easier life than those birds!

"Mom!" Lily said suddenly. "Let's do something for those birds! They look so cold, and there's really not much for them to eat out there."

"Hmm . . . I think I remember there being an old birdfeeder in the garage. I'll go find it."

Lily passed a pleasant day fixing up and filling the birdfeeder. She and her mother attached it to the branch of an oak tree. Then Lily spent the rest of the day looking out the kitchen window as the birds daintily ate the seeds.

Complete the Forming Generalizations Worksheet for the story.

© HMH Supplemental Publishers Inc. All rights reserved.

Forming Generalizations Worksheet

Reading Title _____

Complete the Generalization Pyramid based on what you've read.

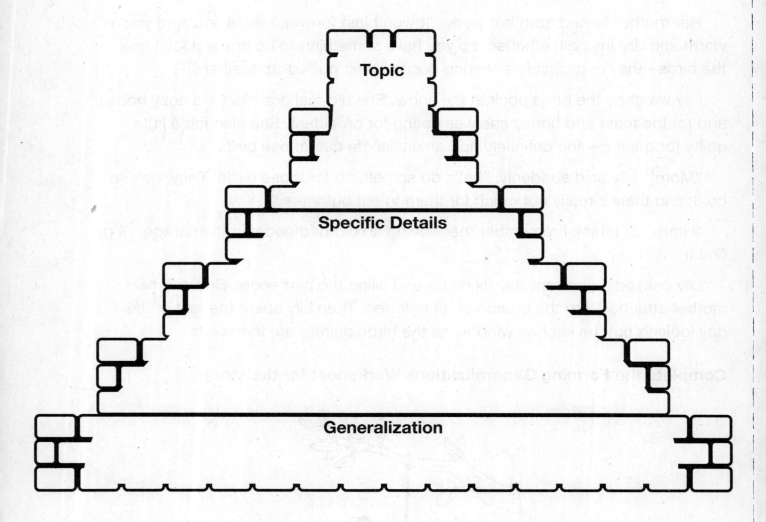

Topic

Specific Details

Generalization

Summary: Use the information in the Generalization Pyramid to write a summary of the reading selection.

_____

_____

Possible Answers

Page 6
Earthquakes

Topic: These paragraphs are about ___earthquakes___

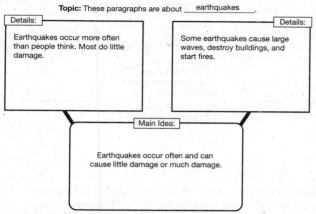

Details: Earthquakes occur more often than people think. Most do little damage.

Details: Some earthquakes cause large waves, destroy buildings, and start fires.

Main Idea: Earthquakes occur often and can cause little damage or much damage.

Summary: Many earthquakes occur every year, and some cause great damage.

Page 7
Food Fuel

Topic: These paragraphs are about ___food as fuel___

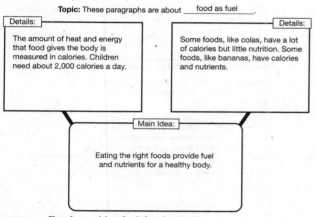

Details: The amount of heat and energy that food gives the body is measured in calories. Children need about 2,000 calories a day.

Details: Some foods, like colas, have a lot of calories but little nutrition. Some foods, like bananas, have calories and nutrients.

Main Idea: Eating the right foods provide fuel and nutrients for a healthy body.

Summary: Food provides fuel for the body.

Page 10
All About Myths

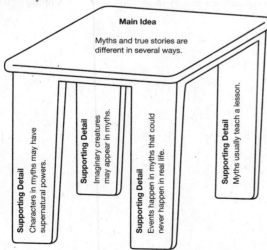

Main Idea
Myths and true stories are different in several ways.

Supporting Detail Characters in myths may have supernatural powers.

Supporting Detail Imaginary creatures may appear in myths.

Supporting Detail Events happen in myths that could never happen in real life.

Supporting Detail Myths usually teach a lesson.

Summary: Myths and true stories are different in several ways. Characters in myths may have supernatural powers. Imaginary creatures may appear in myths.

Page 11
Almost Human

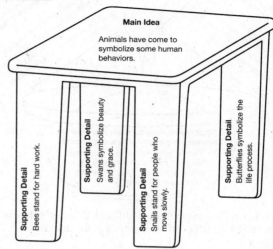

Main Idea
Animals have come to symbolize some human behaviors.

Supporting Detail Bees stand for hard work.

Supporting Detail Swans symbolize beauty and grace.

Supporting Detail Snails stand for people who move slowly.

Supporting Detail Butterflies symbolize the life process.

Summary: People have used some animals as symbols for human behavior. Bees symbolize hard work, while butterflies symbolize the life process.

Page 14
The Campfire

Paragraph	Summary
1	Julia and her father are camping, and Julia gets to cook over an open fire for the first time.
2	Julia's father teaches her how to build a fire.
3	Julia's father lights the fire, and they roast hot dogs over it.

Summary: Julia and her father camp. He teaches her how to build and cook over a camp fire.

Page 15
Plant Your Garden

Paragraph	Summary
1	Start to garden by choosing a sunny patch of good soil that you can water.
2	Get the soil ready for planting by breaking up and fertilizing the soil.
3	Plant seeds in small holes and wait for them to sprout.

Summary: A lot of work goes into a garden before planting seeds. Finding the right soil and preparing it are very important.

© HMH Supplemental Publishers Inc. All rights reserved.
Summarizing Strategies Grade 5, SV 9781419099892

Page 18
Oh, No! Not Again!

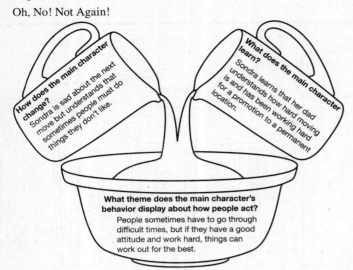

How does the main character change?
Sondra is sad about the next move but understands that sometimes people must do things they don't like.

What does the main character learn?
Sondra learns that her dad understands how hard moving is and has been working hard for a promotion to a permanent location.

What theme does the main character's behavior display about how people act?
People sometimes have to go through difficult times, but if they have a good attitude and work hard, things can work out for the best.

Summary: People can get through difficult changes if they work together and help each other, as Sondra and her dad do.

Page 19
What a Mess!

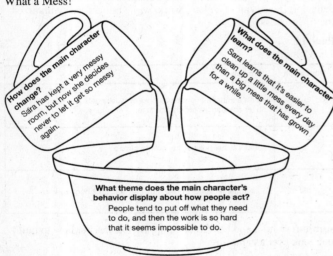

How does the main character change?
Sara has kept a very messy room, but now she decides never to let it get so messy again.

What does the main character learn?
Sara learns that it's easier to clean up a little mess every day than a big mess that has grown for a while.

What theme does the main character's behavior display about how people act?
People tend to put off what they need to do, and then the work is so hard that it seems impossible to do.

Summary: If people take care of little things regularly, such as daily chores, the work is easier than if the chores are all piled together at once.

Page 22
Mom's Birthday

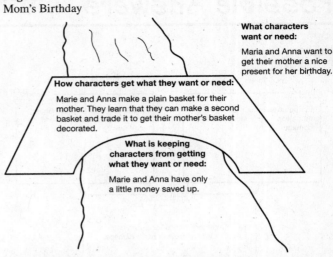

What characters want or need:
Maria and Anna want to get their mother a nice present for her birthday.

How characters get what they want or need:
Marie and Anna make a plain basket for their mother. They learn that they can make a second basket and trade it to get their mother's basket decorated.

What is keeping characters from getting what they want or need:
Marie and Anna have only a little money saved up.

Summary: Maria and Anna make a basket for their mother's birthday present because they don't have the money to buy something. Their basket is so nice that they can make another and trade it to get their mother's basket decorated.

Page 23
Stage Fright

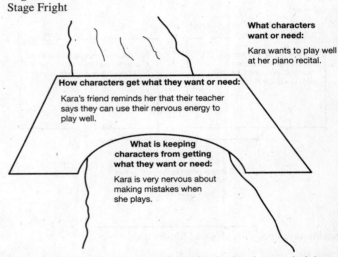

What characters want or need:
Kara wants to play well at her piano recital.

How characters get what they want or need:
Kara's friend reminds her that their teacher says they can use their nervous energy to play well.

What is keeping characters from getting what they want or need:
Kara is very nervous about making mistakes when she plays.

Summary: Kara is nervous about playing in the piano recital, but she uses her nervous energy to perform well and is proud of her performance.

© HMH Supplemental Publishers Inc. All rights reserved.

Page 26
Such a Day!

Topic: _____ A Bad Day _____

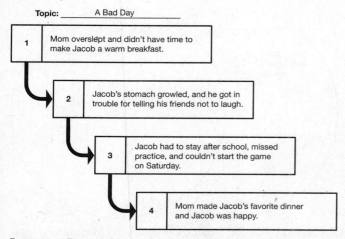

1	Mom overslept and didn't have time to make Jacob a warm breakfast.
2	Jacob's stomach growled, and he got in trouble for telling his friends not to laugh.
3	Jacob had to stay after school, missed practice, and couldn't start the game on Saturday.
4	Mom made Jacob's favorite dinner and Jacob was happy.

Summary: Because his day started out late, Jacob ended up missing ball practice and won't be able to start in the game on Saturday.

Page 27
The Big Test

Topic: _____ Getting Ready to Take a Test _____

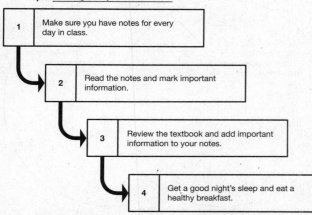

1	Make sure you have notes for every day in class.
2	Read the notes and mark important information.
3	Review the textbook and add important information to your notes.
4	Get a good night's sleep and eat a healthy breakfast.

Summary: By studying your notes, reviewing the textbook, getting a good night's sleep, and eating a healthy breakfast, you can prepare for the big test.

Page 30
Oliver's Pots

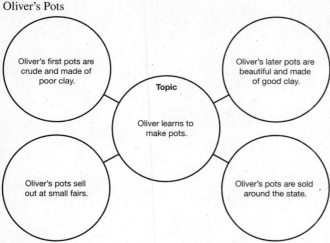

Oliver's first pots are crude and made of poor clay.

Oliver's later pots are beautiful and made of good clay.

Topic: Oliver learns to make pots.

Oliver's pots sell out at small fairs.

Oliver's pots are sold around the state.

Summary: Through practice, Oliver learned to make beautiful pots that many people want to buy.

Page 31
Autumn Leaves

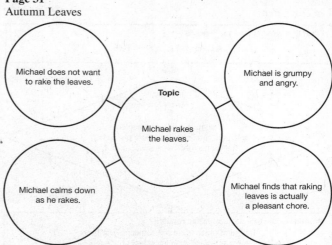

Michael does not want to rake the leaves.

Michael is grumpy and angry.

Topic: Michael rakes the leaves.

Michael calms down as he rakes.

Michael finds that raking leaves is actually a pleasant chore.

Summary: Although at first Michael does not want to rake leaves, he finds that the chore is more pleasant and even more fun than he had thought it would be.

Page 34
Dear Mr. Aggens

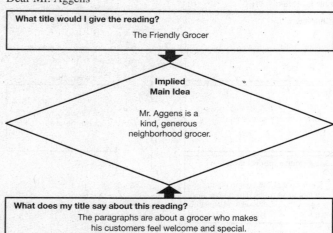

| What title would I give the reading? |
| The Friendly Grocer |

Implied Main Idea

Mr. Aggens is a kind, generous neighborhood grocer.

| What does my title say about this reading? |
| The paragraphs are about a grocer who makes his customers feel welcome and special. |

Summary: The speaker tells about his neighborhood grocer, Mr. Aggens, who talks with his customers and is generous with his time and his knowledge about groceries.

Page 35
The Campaign

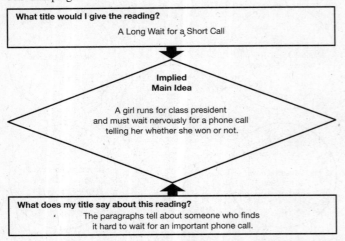

What title would I give the reading?

A Long Wait for a Short Call

Implied Main Idea

A girl runs for class president and must wait nervously for a phone call telling her whether she won or not.

What does my title say about this reading?

The paragraphs tell about someone who finds it hard to wait for an important phone call.

Summary: Kay runs for class president but is worried that she won't be elected. Finally, she receives a phone call that lets her know she won.

Page 38
The Catcher's Mitt

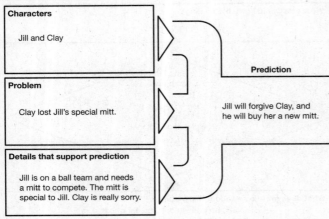

Characters

Jill and Clay

Problem

Clay lost Jill's special mitt.

Details that support prediction

Jill is on a ball team and needs a mitt to compete. The mitt is special to Jill. Clay is really sorry.

Prediction

Jill will forgive Clay, and he will buy her a new mitt.

Summary: Clay borrowed his sister's special mitt without asking her, and then he lost it. He offered to get her a new one.

Page 39
Curtain Time

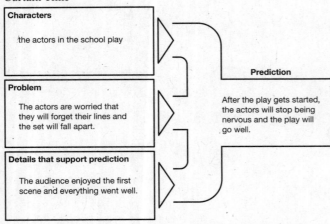

Characters

the actors in the school play

Problem

The actors are worried that they will forget their lines and the set will fall apart.

Details that support prediction

The audience enjoyed the first scene and everything went well.

Prediction

After the play gets started, the actors will stop being nervous and the play will go well.

Summary: The actors in the school play are nervous about forgetting their lines or the set breaking, but the play goes well. People applaud and laugh happily.

Page 42
Mondays and Saturdays

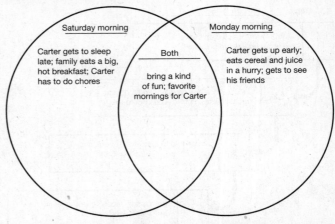

Saturday morning

Carter gets to sleep late; family eats a big, hot breakfast; Carter has to do chores

Both

bring a kind of fun; favorite mornings for Carter

Monday morning

Carter gets up early; eats cereal and juice in a hurry; gets to see his friends

Summary: Carter likes Saturday mornings and Monday mornings. On Saturdays he sleeps late, eats a hot breakfast, and does chores, while on Mondays he gets up early, eats a cold breakfast, and goes to school where he will see his friends.

Page 43
Summer or Winter

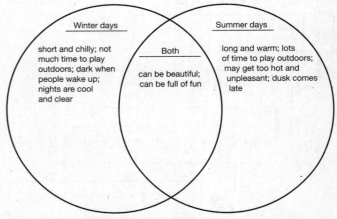

Winter days

short and chilly; not much time to play outdoors; dark when people wake up; nights are cool and clear

Both

can be beautiful; can be full of fun

Summer days

long and warm; lots of time to play outdoors; may get too hot and unpleasant; dusk comes late

Summary: Summer days and winter days can be beautiful and fun. Summer days are longer, with more time to play outdoors, however, they can be so hot that it is not pleasant to stay outside.

Page 46
Central Texas Planting Guide

What is the graphic's title?	Central Texas Planting Guide
What question does the graphic answer? (What is the graphic's main idea?)	plants gardeners should plant each month
What are the most important supporting details in the graphic?	each month along with its plant are equally important

Summary: You must plant each kind of plant during the correct month for a successful garden.

Page 47
Surf's Up!

What is the graphic's title?	Surf's Up!
What question does the graphic answer? (What is the graphic's main idea?)	events and dates for surfing become a popular sport
What are the most important supporting details in the graphic?	1777, James Cook sees wave riders; 1920, Kahanamoku begins competing; 1959, beach movies start craze; 1983, surf schools

Summary: Though people have surfed for at least 300 years, surfing has only recently become popular as a sport.

Page 50
Words and Pictures

Character(s): Alberto		
Details about how character(s) looks	Details about how character(s) acts	Details about the personality of the character(s)
There are few details about Alberto's appearance. He is a boy.	Alberto acts with confidence and creativity. He wants to write a book, so he does just that. He also is willing and happy to work with others.	Alberto has patience and determination. It took time to come up with an idea and a lot of time to write and revise the book.

Summary: Alberto is a boy who is determined to write a book. He is patient and creative enough to succeed.

Page 51
Reading Contest

Character(s): Ronnie		
Details about how character(s) looks	Details about how character(s) acts	Details about the personality of the character(s)
He is a boy that is about 10 or 11 years old.	He reads a lot, and studies to make good grades. He seems excited about reading.	Ronnie is happy, enjoys having hobbies, and likes to learn.

Summary: Ronnie is an elementary school boy who enjoys many hobbies, both doing them and reading about them.

Page 54
Making Room for Baby

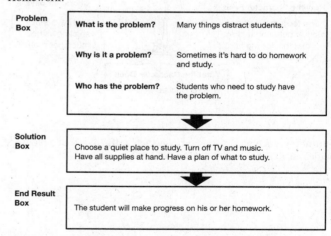

Problem Box	What is the problem?	There is no room in the house for the new baby's bedroom.
	Why is it a problem?	The family does not want to move.
	Who has the problem?	The Juarez family has the problem.

Solution Box — The family decides to make the attic playroom into a bedroom.

End Result Box — The family works together to create a pretty room for the baby, and they don't have to move.

Summary: The Juarez family solves the problem of needing a room for baby by converting the attic into a little bedroom.

Page 55
Homework!

Problem Box	What is the problem?	Many things distract students.
	Why is it a problem?	Sometimes it's hard to do homework and study.
	Who has the problem?	Students who need to study have the problem.

Solution Box — Choose a quiet place to study. Turn off TV and music. Have all supplies at hand. Have a plan of what to study.

End Result Box — The student will make progress on his or her homework.

Summary: It can be hard to focus on doing homework, but studying in a quiet place free of distractions and using a plan will help get the work done.

© HMH Supplemental Publishers Inc. All rights reserved.
Summarizing Strategies Grade 5, SV 9781419099892

Page 58
A Kitten for Julie

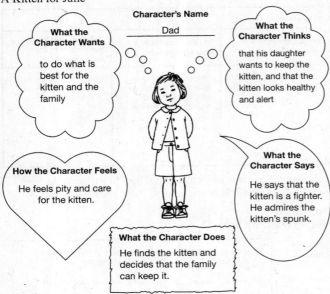

Character's Name
Dad

What the Character Wants
to do what is best for the kitten and the family

What the Character Thinks
that his daughter wants to keep the kitten, and that the kitten looks healthy and alert

How the Character Feels
He feels pity and care for the kitten.

What the Character Says
He says that the kitten is a fighter. He admires the kitten's spunk.

What the Character Does
He finds the kitten and decides that the family can keep it.

Summary: Dad is a caring man who listens to his children and who takes care of situations quickly and confidently.

Page 59
The White Blouse

Character's Name
Jocelyn

What the Character Wants
a new white blouse

What the Character Thinks
She is frustrated at outgrowing her clothes and at how hard it is to find the right blouse. She seems to think her mother is to blame.

How the Character Feels
She feels angry at her mother but soon realizes that this feeling is unfair and apologizes.

What the Character Says
She says that she knows how much her mother does for her.

What the Character Does
She reconciles with her mother.

Summary: Jocelyn is young girl who acts selfishly about a blouse but learns to appreciate the efforts of her mother.

Page 62
The Great Outdoors

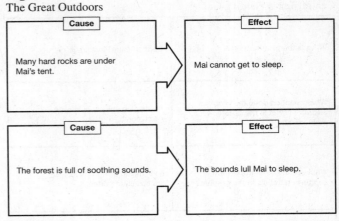

Cause	Effect
Many hard rocks are under Mai's tent.	Mai cannot get to sleep.

Cause	Effect
The forest is full of soothing sounds.	The sounds lull Mai to sleep.

Summary: Conditions in the outdoors affect Mai's ability to sleep.

Page 63
Scary Sleepover

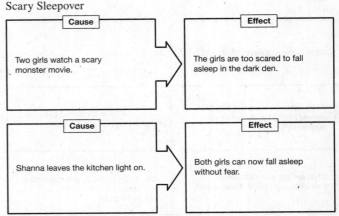

Cause	Effect
Two girls watch a scary monster movie.	The girls are too scared to fall asleep in the dark den.

Cause	Effect
Shanna leaves the kitchen light on.	Both girls can now fall asleep without fear.

Summary: A scary movie keeps two girls from falling asleep, but a little light relieves their fears.

Page 66
Rain, Rain, Come Today

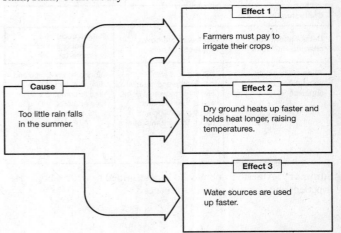

Cause
Too little rain falls in the summer.

Effect 1
Farmers must pay to irrigate their crops.

Effect 2
Dry ground heats up faster and holds heat longer, raising temperatures.

Effect 3
Water sources are used up faster.

Summary: Too little rain in the summer causes problems for farmers, for people enduring the heat, and for cities that get water from rainfall.

© HMH Supplemental Publishers Inc. All rights reserved.
Possible Answers
Summarizing Strategies Grade 5, SV 9781419099892

Page 67
Diana's First Day

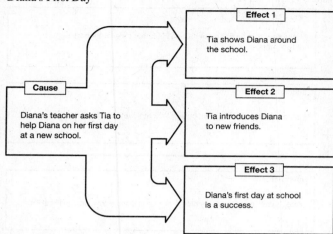

Cause

Diana's teacher asks Tia to help Diana on her first day at a new school.

Effect 1

Tia shows Diana around the school.

Effect 2

Tia introduces Diana to new friends.

Effect 3

Diana's first day at school is a success.

Summary: A nervous student's first day at her new school is a success because of a new friend's help.

Page 70
Tippy the Busy Puppy

Facts	Opinions
Puppies require a lot of care.	Tippy is an annoying puppy.
Joy has a new puppy to care for.	Tippy barks politely.
Tippy wakes Joy up for breakfast.	Having a puppy is worth the trouble.
Tippy checks the back yard each day.	A ball covered with mud and dog slobber is no fun to throw.
Tippy digs holes.	It's so fun to watch him chase his tail.
Tippy barks when someone comes to the door.	
Tippy plays fetch and chases his tail.	
Tippy makes Joy laugh.	

Summary: Though Joy works hard to care for Tippy, her busy puppy, he makes her happy.

Page 71
When Dinosaurs Roamed

Facts	Opinions
Dinosaurs once roamed the world.	It is hard to imagine dinosaurs roaming the world.
We know about dinosaurs from fossils and imprints.	Fossil hunting is a lot of fun.
Fossil hunting can be dangerous and tiring.	The little ones must have been cute.
Dinosaurs ranged from the size of roosters to the size of houses.	It's a good thing that all the dinosaurs are now extinct.
Fossils of teeth show that some dinosaurs ate plants and others ate meat.	It would be strange to share our world with them today.
Dinosaurs lived on land and in the water and even glided on air.	Even their bones are scary.

Summary: Dinosaurs of many kinds once roamed the earth. Fossils and imprints tell us about their sizes, diets, and habitats.

Page 74
That's a Real Brand Name

To Inform	To Entertain
Did I learn something as I read?	Did I smile or laugh as I read?
✓ Yes ___ No	___ Yes ✓ No
To Persuade Me to Think	**To Persuade Me to Act**
Did the reading ask me to change what I think about something?	Did the reading ask me to do something or change my behavior?
___ Yes ✓ No	___ Yes ✓ No

Summary: The purpose of these paragraphs is to inform readers about the practice of branding cattle and some arguments for and against the practice.

Page 75
Park Clean-Up Saturday!

To Inform	To Entertain
Did I learn something as I read?	Did I smile or laugh as I read?
✓ Yes ___ No	___ Yes ✓ No
To Persuade Me to Think	**To Persuade Me to Act**
Did the reading ask me to change what I think about something?	Did the reading ask me to do something or change my behavior?
___ Yes ✓ No	✓ Yes ___ No

Summary: The purpose of this flyer is to inform readers about the clean-up day and to persuade them to help to clean up the park.

© HMH Supplemental Publishers Inc. All rights reserved.
Possible Answers
Summarizing Strategies Grade 5, SV 9781419099892

Page 78
Seasons in the Park

Conclusion: The park is in a city that has harsh, long winters.

Leading Information: Details about icy swings and cold winds in winter and about frost in spring support this conclusion.

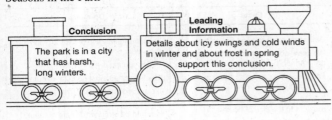

Conclusion: The author knows the park well and is fond of it.

Leading Information: The author describes the park in every season and calls the park "lonely" during the winter.

Summary: The author's park is a special place to him and to the people of the city, even in the winter when weather empties the park.

Page 79
Maria Bakes

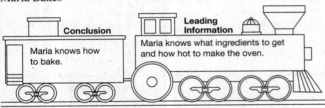

Conclusion: Maria knows how to bake.

Leading Information: Maria knows what ingredients to get and how hot to make the oven.

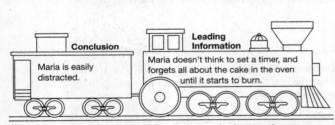

Conclusion: Maria is easily distracted.

Leading Information: Maria doesn't think to set a timer, and forgets all about the cake in the oven until it starts to burn.

Summary: Maria has the skill to bake a cake but needs to pay attention to what she is doing.

Page 82
Prairie Dogs

First Clue: Prairie dog populations decreased.

Second Clue: People regarded prairie dogs as pests.

Inference: Prairie dogs were exterminated in large numbers.

Summary: Prairie dog populations used to be very large, but have decreased greatly over the last few decades. Without understanding the prairie dog's habitat, people have tried to get rid of them.

Page 83
Mateo's Lawn Service

First Clue: Mateo says that he has been helping his father care for their lawn for two years.

Second Clue: Mateo invites people to drive by and look at their lawn.

Inference: Mateo's lawn must look very nice, since he is using it to advertise his skills.

Summary: Though Mateo does not say that his lawn looks nice, it must, because he invites people to look at it as an example of his work.

Page 86
Learning to Carve Wood

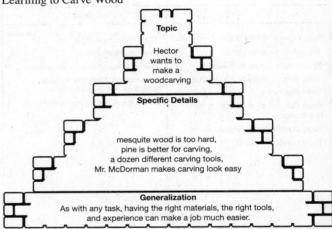

Topic: Hector wants to make a woodcarving

Specific Details: mesquite wood is too hard, pine is better for carving, a dozen different carving tools, Mr. McDorman makes carving look easy

Generalization: As with any task, having the right materials, the right tools, and experience can make a job much easier.

Summary: Hector tries to carve a bear out of wood, but has trouble. He gets advice and help from an experienced woodworker and the task gets much easier.

Page 87
Birds in the Snow

Topic: Lily's feelings about winter

Specific Details: sighing because she can't play outside, griping about the weather, feeling grateful for her warm house, feeling sorry for the birds, feeling glad that she helped the birds

Generalization: Even when situations are not good, people can find something to be happy about and something useful to do.

Summary: Lily has a wide range of feelings about the winter's day, ranging from disappointment and irritation to gratitude and gladness.

© HMH Supplemental Publishers Inc. All rights reserved.

Possible Answers
Summarizing Strategies Grade 5, SV 9781419099892